TEACHER EDITION

GO MATH!

Curious George by Margret and H.A. Rey. Copyright © 2010 by Houghton Mifflin Harcourt Publishing Company. All rights reserved. The character Curious George®, including without limitation the character's name and the character's likenesses, are registered trademarks of Houghton Mifflin Harcourt Publishing Company.

Copyright © 2012 by Houghton Mifflin Harcourt Publishing Company.

Printed in U.S.A.

ISBN 978-0-547-59150-6

7 8 9 10 0877 20 19 18 17 16 15 14 13 12

4500360450   C D E F G

HOUGHTON MIFFLIN HARCOURT

Addition and Subtraction

CRITICAL AREA Building fluency with addition and subtraction

Table of Contents

Chapter 3   Basic Facts and Relationships

 COMMON CORE **Domain:**
Operations and Algebraic Thinking   **CC.2.OA**

PROFESSIONAL DEVELOPMENT

Mathematical Practices:

CC.K–12.MP.2   Reason abstractly and quantitatively.

CC.K–12.MP.3   Construct viable arguments and critique the reasoning of others.

* This chapter also includes the following standards: CC.2.NBT.5, CC.2.MD.6

Addition and Subtraction

CRITICAL AREA Building fluency with addition and subtraction

COMMON CORE PROFESSIONAL DEVELOPMENT

See Teaching for Depth, pp. 117E, 169E, 225E, and 277E.

See Mathematical Practices, pp. 139, 153A, 207, 217A, 243, 257A, 289A, and 307.

Digital Path

GREAT ON INTERACTIVE WHITEBOARD!

1 PLAN

eTeacher Edition

- Access all Teacher Edition pages at school or home

Chapter ePlanner

- Daily Digital Path links to all online resources for each lesson
- Create customized planning calendar
- View and assign online activities and lessons to students

Professional Development Video Podcasts

- Download video podcasts with strategies for teaching concepts and skills
- View on hand-held device or computer

2 ENGAGE

iTools

- Solve problems with interactive digital manipulatives
- Model and explore lesson math concepts

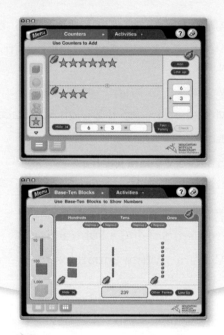

HMH Mega Math

- Provides additional lesson practice with engaging activities that include audio and animation

3 TEACH

● *e*Student Edition

- Includes all Student Edition pages for student access at school or home
- Provides audio reinforcement for each lesson
- Features point-of-use links to Animated Math Models

● Multimedia *e*Glossary

- Includes audio, graphics, and animation

● Animated Math Models

- Curious George introduces interactive lesson activities with audio and animation
- Concepts are modeled and reinforced with feedback

4 ASSESS

● Online Assessment System

- Receive instant results, including prescriptions for intervention
- Includes a variety of reports to track student progress
- Create customized tests

▲ RtI Response to Intervention

● Soar to Success Math

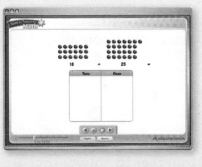

- Diagnose and prescribe interactive intervention lessons for all **RtI** Tiers

Tier 1	On-Level Intervention
Tier 2	Strategic Intervention
Tier 3	Intensive Intervention

21ST CENTURY SKILLS

Go Math! Digital Path provides the opportunity for lifelong learning skills for students in the 21st Century by developing:

- **Information and communication skills**
- **Higher order thinking skills**
- **Problem solving skills**
- **Independent learners**
- **Real-world connections**

1 READ

All About Animals

Objective Use literature to review addition concepts.

Genre Nonfiction

Domains: Operations and Algebraic Thinking
Number and Operations in Base Ten

▶ **Preparing to Read** Refer children to the story cover and read the title. Have children flip through the pages and identify the animals on each page.

Explain that they will read the story together and solve math problems. Then they will read the story again and learn some fun animal facts. They will use the facts to help them answer science questions about how animals care for their young.

▶ **Story Vocabulary** giraffe, ostrich, kangaroo, mobs, wild boars, snout, sounders, moose, antlers, gallop

▶ **Reading the Math Story**
Pages 109–112

Each story passage describes two groups. The groups must be added together to answer the question on each page.

- **What number sentence can you write to find the number of giraffes in all? Explain.**
  5 + 5 = 10; there are two groups and there are five in each group, so you add to find the sum.

- **What number sentence can you write to find the total number of eggs in the nest?**
  6 + 5 = 11 or 5 + 6 = 11

- **What number sentence can you write to find the total number of kangaroos in the mob?** 8 + 4 = 12 or 4 + 8 = 12

Addition and Subtraction

CRITICAL AREA

All About Animals
by John Hudson

COMMON CORE **CRITICAL AREA** Building fluency with addition and subtraction

109

The giraffe is the tallest land animal in the world. Adult giraffes are 13 to 17 feet tall. Newborn giraffes are about 6 feet tall.

A group of 5 giraffes drinks water at a watering hole. A group of 5 giraffes eats leaves from trees. How many giraffes are there in all?

_10_ giraffes

110   How do giraffes care for their young?

The ostrich is the largest bird in the world. Ostriches cannot fly, but they can run fast. Ostrich eggs weigh about 3 pounds each! Several ostriches will lay eggs in a shared nest.

There are 6 eggs in a nest. Then 5 more eggs are put in that nest. How many eggs are in the nest now?

_11_ eggs

How do ostriches care for their young?   111

Kangaroos can move quickly by jumping with their two back legs. When they are moving slowly, they use all four legs.

Western gray kangaroos live in groups called mobs. There are 8 kangaroos in a mob. 4 more kangaroos join the mob. How many kangaroos are in the mob in all?

_12_ kangaroos

112   How do kangaroos care for their young?

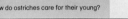

Page 113

Wild boars like to eat roots. They use their tough snouts to dig. Wild boars can be up to 6 feet long.

Wild boars live in groups called sounders. There is one sounder of 14 boars. If 7 of the boars are eating, how many boars are not eating?

_____7_____ boars

How do wild boars care for their young? 113

Page 114

Moose are the largest kind of deer. Male moose have antlers that may be 5 to 6 feet wide. Moose can trot and gallop. They are also good swimmers!

A ranger saw 7 moose in the morning and 6 moose in the afternoon. How many moose did the ranger see that day?

_____13_____ moose

How do moose care for their young?

Page 115

Name _____

Write About the Story

Choose one kind of animal. Draw a picture and write your own story about that kind of animal. Use addition in your story.

Vocabulary Review
add   in all

giraffe   ostrich   kangaroo   Check children's work.

Write Math

115

Page 116

How many eggs are there?

Draw more ostrich eggs in each nest. Write an addition sentence below each nest to show how many eggs are in each nest now. Check children's work.

Math Board → Choose a different animal from the story. Write another story that uses addition.

116

Pages 113 and 114

Children should understand the story progression. Have children share how they solved each problem.

- **How did you find the number of boars not eating?** Possible answer: I knew that 7 boars were eating and that there were 14 boars in all, so I thought 7 plus how many more is 14. I know that $7 + 7 = 14$.

- **What addition strategy could you use to find the total number of moose?** Possible answer: I need to add 7 and 6 so I could double 6 and then add 1.

2 RESPOND

Write About the Story

Page 115

Write Math   Ask children to choose one animal from the story. Have them draw a picture and write a story about their animal. Encourage children to use addition and the review vocabulary in their stories. Ask volunteers to share their stories with the class.

▶ **Math Vocabulary** add, in all

Do the Math

▶ **How many eggs are there?**

Page 116

In this activity, children draw additional eggs in each ostrich nest and write addition sentences to match. Then challenge children to write another addition story about a different animal.

 Connections to Science

Read the story again as children follow along. Then read aloud the fun facts about animals listed below. Have children look at the story pictures and discuss the Science question on each page.

Giraffe Facts:

- Newborn giraffes are hidden for their first month of life to protect them from other animals.
- After about two months, baby calves are left in "nursery groups" while the mothers feed.

Ostrich Facts:

- Ostriches use their bodies to protect their young. For example, adult ostriches cover chicks with their wings. This protects the chicks from the sun, rain, and dangerous animals.
- Ostriches use their long necks and good eyesight to watch for danger.

Kangaroo Facts:

- Kangaroos keep their young in a special place. This place is a mother's front pouch.
- Baby kangaroos are called joeys. They stay inside their mothers' pouches for 7–10 months.
- Joeys grow inside the pouch until they are ready to stand up on their own.

Moose Facts:

- Moose calves are able to follow their mother hours after being born.
- The mother moose stays with her calf for about one year.
- The mother helps her calf by feeding it the healthiest plants she can find.

Wild Boar Facts:

- Mother wild boars are called sows.
- Sows get together in groups to protect their piglets from danger.
- The sows form a circle and place their piglets in the center.

The Project

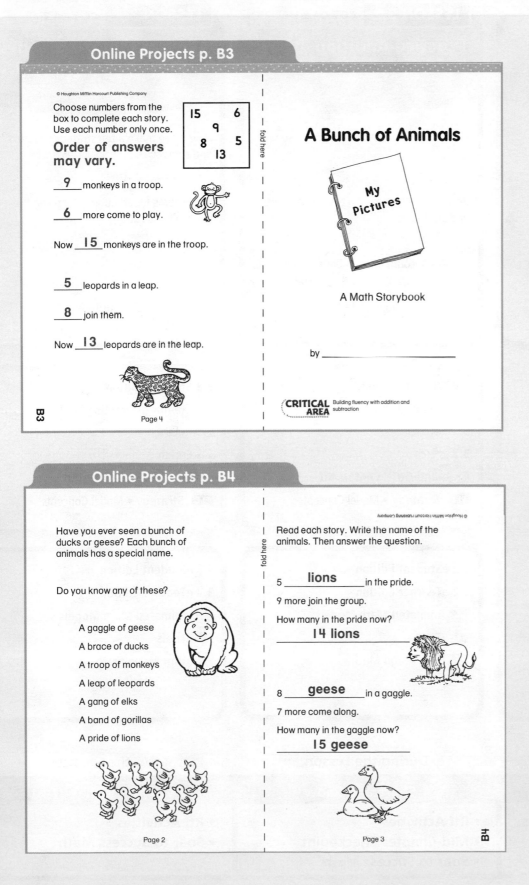

© Houghton Mifflin Harcourt Publishing Company

Choose numbers from the box to complete each story. Use each number only once.

15		6
	9	
8		5
	13	

Order of answers may vary.

___9___ monkeys in a troop.

___6___ more come to play.

Now __15__ monkeys are in the troop.

___5___ leopards in a leap.

___8___ join them.

Now __13__ leopards are in the leap.

B3   Page 4

A Bunch of Animals

My Pictures

A Math Storybook

by _____

CRITICAL AREA Building fluency with addition and subtraction

Have you ever seen a bunch of ducks or geese? Each bunch of animals has a special name.

Do you know any of these?

A gaggle of geese
A brace of ducks
A troop of monkeys
A leap of leopards
A gang of elks
A band of gorillas
A pride of lions

Page 2

© Houghton Mifflin Harcourt Publishing Company

Read each story. Write the name of the animals. Then answer the question.

5 ___lions___ in the pride.

9 more join the group.

How many in the pride now?

__14 lions__

8 ___geese___ in a gaggle.

7 more come along.

How many in the gaggle now?

__15 geese__

Page 3   B4

My Math Storybook

A Bunch of Animals

Objective Review addition facts.

Materials Online Projects pp. B3–B4, crayons

Print and copy the pages from the Online Projects and help children fold them to make their own storybooks. Explain that they will work together to complete stories about groups of animals.

Remind children that a group of kangaroos is called a mob, and a group of boars is called a sounder. Page 2 of the storybook lists special names for some other groups of animals. Have children follow along as you read the list.

On page 3, children fill in the missing names of the animals and answer story questions. Have them refer back to page 2 for help with animal group names.
On page 4, children write numbers to complete each animal story. Tell them to choose numbers from the box and not to repeat any numbers.

After children have completed the pages, have them share their work with the class, and then take their storybooks home to share with family members.

 You may suggest that children place completed projects in their portfolios.

Chapter At A Glance

Domain: Operations and Algebraic Thinking

Chapter Essential Question How can you use patterns and strategies to find sums and differences for basic facts?

Use the Chapter Planner in the *Go Math! Planning Guide* for pacing.

Lesson At A Glance

	LESSON 3.1 CC.2.OA.2	**LESSON 3.2** CC.2.OA.2	**LESSON 3.3** CC.2.OA.2
	Use Doubles Facts 121A	**Practice Addition Facts** 125A	**Algebra • Make a Ten to Add** 129A
Essential Question	How can you use doubles facts to find sums for near doubles facts?	What are some ways to remember sums?	How is the make a ten strategy used to find sums?
Objective	Use doubles facts as a strategy for finding sums for near doubles facts.	Recall sums for basic facts using properties and strategies.	Recall sums for addition facts using the make a ten strategy.
Vocabulary	**sums**, doubles	**addends**, count on, number sentence	
Materials	MathBoard, Counting Tape	MathBoard, Counting Tape	MathBoard, Counting Tape

Print Resources

3.1 Student Edition	3.2 Student Edition	3.3 Student Edition
3.1 Standards Practice Book	3.2 Standards Practice Book	3.3 Standards Practice Book
3.1 Reteach	3.2 Reteach	3.3 Reteach
3.1 Enrich	3.2 Enrich	3.3 Enrich
Grab-and-Go™ Centers Kit	Grab-and-Go™ Centers Kit	Grab-and-Go™ Centers Kit
ELL Strategy • Draw	**ELL** Strategy • Model Concepts	**ELL** Strategy • Model Concepts

Digital Path

3.1 *eStudent Edition*	3.2 *eStudent Edition*	3.3 *eStudent Edition*
3.1 *eTeacher Edition*	3.2 *eTeacher Edition*	3.3 *eTeacher Edition*
Animated Math Models	Animated Math Models	Animated Math Models
iT iTools	*iT* iTools	*iT* iTools
HMH Mega Math	HMH Mega Math	HMH Mega Math

RtI — Response to Intervention

Before the Chapter	**During the Lesson**	**After the Chapter**
✔ **Show What You Know**	✔ **Share and Show**	✔ **Chapter Review/Test**
• Prerequisite Skills Activities	• RtI Activities	• RtI Activities
• Soar to Success Math	• Mid-Chapter Checkpoint	• Soar to Success Math
	• Soar to Success Math	

Use every day to develop computational fluency.
Visit **www.greatsource.com/everydaycounts**

Assess Depth of Knowledge

See Chapter 3 Performance Task and *Assessment Guide*.

LESSON 3.4 CC.2.OA.2

Algebra • Add 3 Addends 133A

How do you add three numbers?

Find sums of three addends by applying the Commutative and Associative Properties of Addition.

sum, addends

MathBoard, Counting Tape

LESSON 3.5 CC.2.OA.2

Algebra • Relate Addition and Subtraction ... 137A

How are addition and subtraction related?

Use the inverse relationship of addition and subtraction to recall basic facts.

differences, related facts

MathBoard, Counting Tape

LESSON 3.6 CC.2.OA.2

Practice Subtraction Facts 141A

What are some ways to remember differences?

Recall differences for basic facts using mental strategies.

count back

MathBoard, Counting Tape

3.4 Student Edition
3.4 Standards Practice Book
3.4 Reteach
3.4 Enrich
Grab-and-Go™ Centers Kit
ELL Strategy • Model Concepts

3.5 Student Edition
3.5 Standards Practice Book
3.5 Reteach
3.5 Enrich
Grab-and-Go™ Centers Kit
ELL Strategy • Identify Relationships

3.6 Student Edition
3.6 Standards Practice Book
3.6 Reteach
3.6 Enrich
Grab-and-Go™ Centers Kit
ELL Strategy • Define

3.4 eStudent Edition
3.4 eTeacher Edition
Animated Math Models
iTools
HMH Mega Math

3.5 eStudent Edition
3.5 eTeacher Edition
Animated Math Models
iTools
HMH Mega Math

3.6 eStudent Edition
3.6 eTeacher Edition
Animated Math Models
iTools
HMH Mega Math

GREAT ON INTERACTIVE WHITEBOARD!

Digital Path

Animated Math Models
Assessment
HMH Mega Math
iTools
Multimedia eGlossary
Professional Development Video Podcasts
Soar to Success Math

Chapter At A Glance

Domain: Operations and Algebraic Thinking

Lesson At A Glance	**LESSON 3.7** CC.2.OA.2	**LESSON 3.8** CC.2.OA.1	**LESSON 3.9** CC.2.OA.1
	Use Ten to Subtract 145A	**Algebra • Use Drawings to Represent Problems 149A**	**Algebra • Use Equations to Represent Problems 153A**
Essential Question	How does getting to 10 in subtraction help when finding differences?	How are bar models used to show addition and subtraction problems?	How are number sentences used to show addition and subtraction situations?
Objective	Find differences on a number line to develop the mental strategy of decomposing to simplify facts.	Use bar models to represent a variety of addition and subtraction situations.	Write equations to represent and solve a variety of addition and subtraction situations.
Vocabulary	difference	bar model	number sentence
Materials	MathBoard, Counting Tape	MathBoard, Counting Tape	MathBoard, Counting Tape

Print Resources			
	3.7 Student Edition	**3.8 Student Edition**	**3.9 Student Edition**
	3.7 Standards Practice Book	**3.8 Standards Practice Book**	**3.9 Standards Practice Book**
	3.7 Reteach	3.8 Reteach	3.9 Reteach
	3.7 Enrich	**3.8 Enrich**	**3.9 Enrich**
	Grab-and-Go™ Centers Kit	**Grab-and-Go™ Centers Kit**	**Grab-and-Go™ Centers Kit**
	ELL Strategy • Describe	**ELL** Strategy • Explore Context	**ELL** Strategy • Explore Context

Digital Path			
	3.7 *eStudent Edition*	3.8 *eStudent Edition*	3.9 *eStudent Edition*
	3.7 *eTeacher Edition*	3.8 *eTeacher Edition*	3.9 *eTeacher Edition*
	iT iTools	Animated Math Models	Animated Math Models
		iT iTools	*iT* iTools
			HMH Mega Math

Assessment	Diagnostic	Formative	Summative
	• **Show What You Know**	• **Lesson Quick Check**	• **Chapter Review/Test**
	• **Diagnostic Interview Task**	• **Mid-Chapter Checkpoint**	• **Performance Assessment**
	• **Soar to Success Math**		• **Chapter Test**
			• **Online Assessment**

LESSON 3.10 CC.2.OA.4

Problem Solving • Equal Groups 157A

How can acting it out help when solving a problem about equal groups?

Solve problems involving equal groups by using the strategy *act it out*.

MathBoard, two color counters, Counting Tape

3.10 Student Edition
3.10 Standards Practice Book
3.10 Reteach
3.10 Enrich
Grab-and-Go™ Centers Kit
ELL **Strategy** • Draw

3.10 *e*Student Edition
3.10 *e*Teacher Edition
HMH Mega Math

LESSON 3.11 CC.2.OA.4

Algebra • Repeated Addition 161A

How can you write an addition sentence for problems with equal groups?

Write equations using repeated addition to find the total number of objects in arrays.

row, addition sentence

MathBoard, two-color counters, Counting Tape

3.11 Student Edition
3.11 Standards Practice Book
3.11 Reteach
3.11 Enrich
Grab-and-Go™ Centers Kit
ELL **Strategy** • Model Language

3.11 *e*Student Edition
3.11 *e*Teacher Edition
Chapter 3 Test
HMH Mega Math

Teacher Notes

COMMON CORE PROFESSIONAL DEVELOPMENT

Teaching for Depth

Matt Larson
Curriculum Specialist for Mathematics
Lincoln Public Schools
Lincoln, Nebraska

Thinking Strategies for Addition

Fluency is based on instructional strategies that are developed conceptually, rather than based on rote practice and memorization (Fuson, 2003; NRC, 2001).

Thinking strategies for addition facts are directly related to one or more number relationships and include the following (Van de Walle, 2004):

+	0	1	2	3	4	5	6	7	8	9
0	0	1	2	3	4	5	6	7	8	9
1	1	2	3	4	5	6	7	8	9	10
2	2	3	4	5	6	7	8	9	10	11
3	3	4	5	6	7	8	9	10	11	12
4	4	5	6	7	8	9	10	11	12	13
5	5	6	7	8	9	10	11	12	13	14
6	6	7	8	9	10	11	12	13	14	15
7	7	8	9	10	11	12	13	14	15	16
8	8	9	10	11	12	13	14	15	16	17
9	9	10	11	12	13	14	15	16	17	18

- Facts that have one addend of 1 or 2 (36 facts).

- Facts that have zero as one of the addends (19 facts).

- Doubles facts (10 facts).

- Make a ten by giving some quantity from one addend to the other addend (Fuson, 2003). This can be enhanced through the ten frame.

From the Research

“ Examining the relationships between addition and subtraction and seeing subtraction as involving a known and unknown addend are examples of adaptive reasoning. By providing experiences for young students to develop adaptive reasoning in addition and subtraction situations, teachers are also anticipating algebra as students begin to appreciate the inverse relationships between the two operations. ” (NRC, 2001, p. 191)

Thinking Strategies for Subtraction

Teaching for understanding is enhanced when instruction focuses on tasks and strategies that help students develop relationships within addition and subtraction combinations (NCTM, 2000).

Learning to think of subtraction as addition can make subtraction as easy as, or easier than, addition (Fuson, 2003).

- Rather than thinking of 14 – 8, children can be encouraged to focus on 8 and what other number make 14.

- This strategy focuses on part-part-whole relations, which have been shown to be particularly effective at supporting students' development of efficient thinking subtraction strategies (NRC, 2001).

- Emphasizing part-part-whole relations helps students develop an understanding of related facts and inverse operations, and their ability to recognize when to add and when to subtract (NRC, 2001).

COMMON CORE Mathematical Practices

Teachers who want to develop deep understanding in their students encourage them to share the strategies they use for addition and subtraction combinations during class discussions. Students develop and refine strategies during math talk as they hear other students' descriptions of their thinking (NCTM, 2000). Discussing their explanations gives children an opportunity to **attend to precision**.

PODCASTING

Professional Development Video Podcasts:
The Meaning of Addition and Subtraction, Grades K–2, Segments 2, 4, 5

Daily Classroom Management

Differentiated Instruction

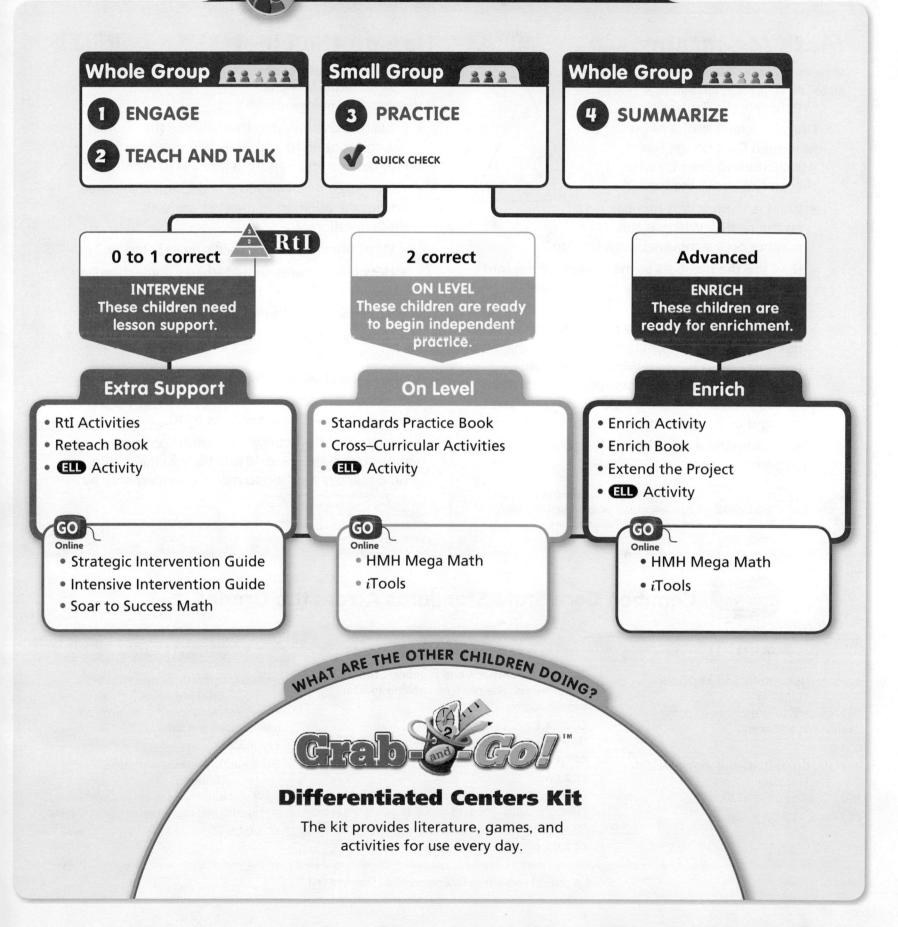

Whole Group

1 ENGAGE

2 TEACH AND TALK

Small Group

3 PRACTICE

✔ QUICK CHECK

Whole Group

4 SUMMARIZE

---

0 to 1 correct — RtI

INTERVENE
These children need lesson support.

2 correct

ON LEVEL
These children are ready to begin independent practice.

Advanced

ENRICH
These children are ready for enrichment.

Extra Support

- RtI Activities
- Reteach Book
- **ELL** Activity

GO Online
- Strategic Intervention Guide
- Intensive Intervention Guide
- Soar to Success Math

On Level

- Standards Practice Book
- Cross–Curricular Activities
- **ELL** Activity

GO Online
- HMH Mega Math
- iTools

Enrich

- Enrich Activity
- Enrich Book
- Extend the Project
- **ELL** Activity

GO Online
- HMH Mega Math
- iTools

WHAT ARE THE OTHER CHILDREN DOING?

Grab-and-Go!™

Differentiated Centers Kit

The kit provides literature, games, and activities for use every day.

Review Prerequisite Skills

RtI Activities

Math Mountains! — TIER 2

Objective Practice addition and subtraction facts to 10.

Materials Math Mountain Cards for facts to 10 (see *eTeacher Resources*)

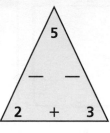

- Draw an example of a Math Mountain Card on the board. Ask children to describe what they notice about the card.

  - **What is the greatest number on the card?** 5 **Where is this number on the mountain?** on the top
  - **How are the numbers at the bottom of the card related to 5?** They can be added together to make 5.
  - **Why is the plus sign at the bottom?** The two numbers on the bottom can be added to make the number on the top. **Why are the minus signs on each side?** Each number on the bottom can be subtracted from the number on the top of the card to get the other number on the card.

- Have children practice addition and subtraction facts with the cards.

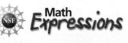

Model from *Math Expressions*. For more information visit www.eduplace.com/hmhschool/mathexpressions

Hop on the Line! — TIER 3

Objective Practice counting on and counting back for addition and subtraction facts to 10.

Materials floor number line, labeled 0–10

- Explain to children that they will use the number line to count on to add. They will stand next to the number line and hop from number to number.

- Tell children they will add 6 and 2. Ask a volunteer to act out the addition as the class answers these questions.

  - **What number should [child's name] start on?** 6
  - **How many spaces should [child's name] hop?** 2 spaces
  - **Where will [child's name] land?** on 8
  - **What number sentence did [child's name] model?** $6 + 2 = 8$

- Ask all the children to write the number sentence.

- Continue the activity with different addition facts, adding 1, 2, or 3 to show sums to 10.

- Then repeat the activity for subtraction facts with start numbers to 10 and have a child begin on a number and hop to model counting back by 1, 2, or 3.

COMMON CORE — Common Core State Standards Across the Grades

Before	Grade 2	After
Domain: Operations and Algebraic Thinking Represent and solve problems involving addition and subtraction. **CC.1.OA.1** **Domain: Operations and Algebraic Thinking** Add and subtract within 20. **CC.1.OA.5, CC.1.OA.6**	**Domain: Operations and Algebraic Thinking** Represent and solve problems involving addition and subtraction. **CC.2.OA.1** **Domain: Operations and Algebraic Thinking** Add and subtract within 20. **CC.2.OA.2** **Domain: Operations and Algebraic Thinking** Work with equal groups of objects to gain foundations for multiplication. **CC.2.OA.4**	**Domain: Operations and Algebraic Thinking** Represent and solve problems involving multiplication and division. **CC.3.OA.1** **Domain: Operations and Algebraic Thinking** Solve problems involving the four operations, and identify and explain patterns in arithmetic. **CC.3.OA.8**

See A page of each lesson for Common Core Standard text.

Developing Math Language

Chapter Vocabulary

sums the answers to addition problems

addends any of the numbers that are added

differences the answers to subtraction problems

 Visualize It
Have children make and complete this chart for each new vocabulary word as they go through the chapter.

Word	
Predicted Meaning	
Meaning	

GO Online Multimedia eGlossary

ELL Vocabulary Activity

Objective Understand the math term *addend*.

Materials Vocabulary Card: *addend* (see *eTeacher Resources*), paper, crayons, pencil

Display several addition facts. Explain that the numbers that are added are called *addends*. Then have children point to each of the addends in the addition facts. Give children a word problem. Have them name the addends in the fact that solves the word problem.

Practice vocabulary by using questioning strategies such as the following:

Beginning
- Show children an addition fact. Have children point to the addends.

Intermediate
- What are the addends in $5 + 7 = 12$? 5 and 7

Advanced
- When adding $8 + 3 + 2 = 13$, what are the addends? 8, 3, 2 Have children write a different problem with three addends.

See ELL Activity Guide for leveled activities.

Vocabulary Strategy • Graphic Organizer

Materials K.I.M. Diagram (see *eTeacher Resources*)
- Write the vocabulary word in the left column.
- Write information about the word in the center column.
- Have children draw a picture, a memory clue, in the right column.

K Key Idea	I Information	M Memory Clue
sums		
addends		
differences		

Chapter 3

Introduce the Chapter

Parrot fish live near coral reefs in tropical ocean waters. They use their sharp teeth to scrape food off of the coral.

Suppose 10 parrot fish are eating at a coral reef. 3 of the fish swim away. How many fish are still eating? **7 fish**

Explore with children some ways to solve the problem. Encourage children to make a variety of suggestions. Then have them work in small groups and use a strategy of their choice to solve.

Additional Facts About Parrot Fish

- Parrot fish have grinding teeth in their throats. They use these teeth to get to food hidden inside the chunks of coral they take from reefs.

- A group of fish is called a school.

Discussion Question

- **Have you ever seen a colorful fish? If you have, describe what it looked like. Where did you see it?** Answers will vary.

Chapter 3 Basic Facts and Relationships

Curious About Math with
Curious George

Parrot fish live near coral reefs in tropical ocean waters. They use their sharp teeth to scrape food off of the coral.

Suppose 10 parrot fish are eating at a coral reef. 3 of the fish swim away. How many fish are still eating?

Chapter 3
one hundred seventeen **117**

Intervention Options  **RtI** Response to Intervention

Use Show What You Know, Lesson Quick Check, and Assessments to diagnose children's intervention levels.

TIER 1	TIER 2	TIER 3	ENRICHMENT
On-Level Intervention	**Strategic Intervention**	**Intensive Intervention**	**Independent Activities**
For children who are generally at grade level but need early intervention with the lesson concepts, use:	For children who need small group instruction to review concepts and skills needed for the chapter, use:	For children who need one-on-one instruction to build foundational skills for the chapter, use:	For children who successfully complete lessons, use:
▲ Tier 1 Activity for every lesson	▲ Tier 2 Activity for every lesson	GO Online Intensive Intervention Guide	**Grab-and-Go!** **Differentiated Centers Kit**
★ Soar to Success Math	GO Online Strategic Intervention Guide	▲ Prerequisite Skills Activities	• Enrich Activity for every lesson
	▲ Prerequisite Skills Activities	★ Soar to Success Math	• Enrich Book
	★ Soar to Success Math		MM HMH Mega Math

Name _____

Show What You Know ✓

Use Symbols to Add

Use the picture. Use + and = to complete the addition sentence.

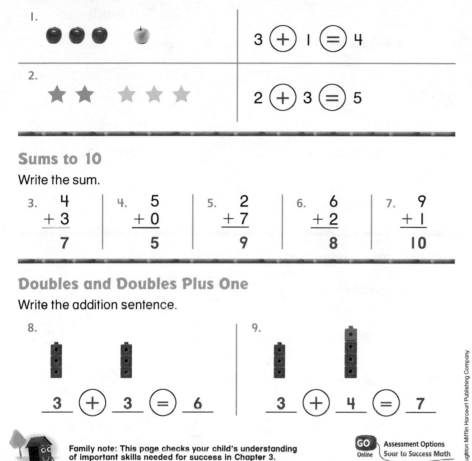

1. 🍎🍎🍎 🍏 $3 \bigoplus 1 \bigoplus = 4$

2. ★★ ★★★ $2 \bigoplus 3 \bigoplus = 5$

Sums to 10

Write the sum.

3.	4.	5.	6.	7.
4 + 3 **7**	5 + 0 **5**	2 + 7 **9**	6 + 2 **8**	9 + 1 **10**

Doubles and Doubles Plus One

Write the addition sentence.

8. $3 \bigoplus + 3 \bigoplus = 6$

9. $3 \bigoplus + 4 \bigoplus = 7$

Family note: This page checks your child's understanding of important skills needed for success in Chapter 3.

GO Online Assessment Options Soar to Success Math

© Houghton Mifflin Harcourt Publishing Company

118 one hundred eighteen

Assessing Prior Knowledge

Have children complete on their own **Show What You Know.** Tested items are the prerequisite skills of this chapter.

Diagnostic Interview Task

The alternative interview tasks below evaluate children's understanding of each **Show What You Know** skill. The diagnostic chart may be used for intervention on prerequisite skills.

Materials two-color counters, connecting cubes

For evaluation checklist see *Assessment Guide.*

Display one blue connecting cube and a train of two red connecting cubes.

- Have the child write a number sentence to show the addition of the cubes. 1 + 2 = 3

Place 4 red counters and 2 yellow counters in front of the child.

- Have the child find the total number of counters. 6 counters

Display two trains of 4 red connecting cubes.

- Have the child write the doubles fact that is modeled with the cubes. 4 + 4 = 8

✓ Show What You Know • Diagnostic Assessment

Use to determine if children need intervention for the chapter's prerequisite skills.

Were children successful with Show What You Know?

If NO...then INTERVENE

If YES...then use INDEPENDENT ACTIVITIES

	Skill	Missed More Than	Intervene With	Soar to Success Math
TIER 3	Use Symbols to Add	0	*Intensive Intervention* Skill 2; *Intensive Intervention User Guide* Activity 3	Warm-Up 10.09
TIER 2	Sums to 10	1	*Strategic Intervention* Skill 5	Warm-Up 10.12
TIER 2	Doubles and Doubles Plus One	0	*Strategic Intervention* Skill 6	Warm-Up 10.18

Grab-and-Go!™

Differentiated Centers Kit

Use the *Enrich Book* or the independent activities in the *Grab-and-Go™ Differentiated Centers Kit.*

Basic Facts and Relationships **118**

Chapter 3

Vocabulary Builder (MATHEMATICAL PRACTICES)

Have children complete the activities on this page by working alone or with partners.

▶ **Visualize It** Make sure children understand that they should sort the Review Words and record them in the Venn diagram. Have children share how they sorted the words and tell how they decided to place each one.

▶ **Understand Vocabulary**

You may want to remind children that addition sentences have a plus sign and subtraction sentences have a minus sign.

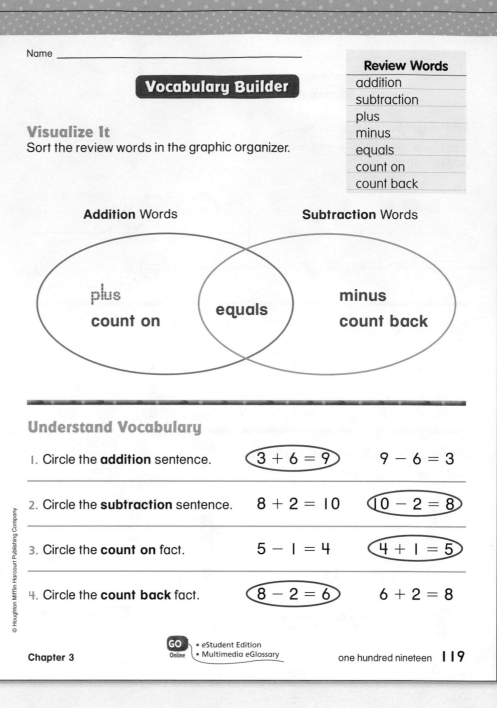

Name _____

Vocabulary Builder

Review Words
addition
subtraction
plus
minus
equals
count on
count back

Visualize It
Sort the review words in the graphic organizer.

Addition Words   **Subtraction** Words

plus
count on   equals   minus
count back

Understand Vocabulary

1. Circle the **addition** sentence.   (3 + 6 = 9)   9 − 6 = 3

2. Circle the **subtraction** sentence.   8 + 2 = 10   (10 − 2 = 8)

3. Circle the **count on** fact.   5 − 1 = 4   (4 + 1 = 5)

4. Circle the **count back** fact.   (8 − 2 = 6)   6 + 2 = 8

© Houghton Mifflin Harcourt Publishing Company

GO Online • eStudent Edition • Multimedia eGlossary

Chapter 3   one hundred nineteen **119**

Vocabulary Preview

Preview with children the following words that will be used in this chapter.

sums   addends   differences

For each preview word, have children try to give the meaning of the word on their own. If they have difficulty, give them a sentence using the word in a context so that its meaning can be determined. Once children have given a correct meaning, have them explain which words in the sentence you gave helped them know the meaning.

119   Chapter 3

Game Caterpillar Chase

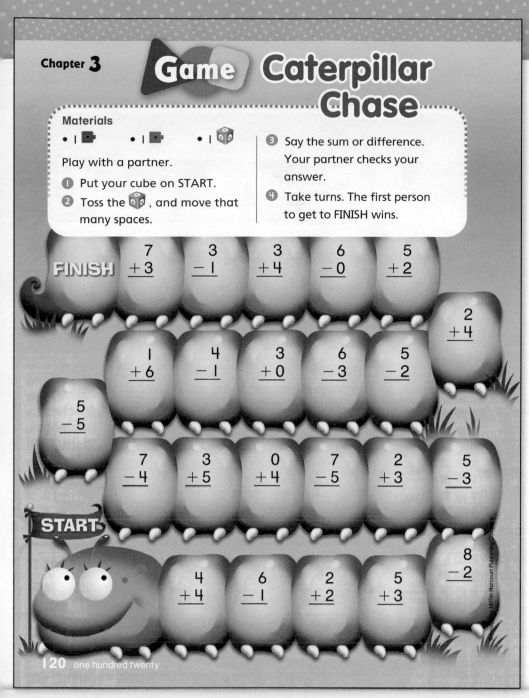

Materials
- I 🔴 • I 🔵 • I 🎲

Play with a partner.

1 Put your cube on START.

2 Toss the 🎲, and move that many spaces.

3 Say the sum or difference. Your partner checks your answer.

4 Take turns. The first person to get to FINISH wins.

FINISH

| $\begin{array}{r}7\\+3\\\hline\end{array}$ | $\begin{array}{r}3\\-1\\\hline\end{array}$ | $\begin{array}{r}3\\+4\\\hline\end{array}$ | $\begin{array}{r}6\\-0\\\hline\end{array}$ | $\begin{array}{r}5\\+2\\\hline\end{array}$ |

$\begin{array}{r}2\\+4\\\hline\end{array}$

| $\begin{array}{r}1\\+6\\\hline\end{array}$ | $\begin{array}{r}4\\-1\\\hline\end{array}$ | $\begin{array}{r}3\\+0\\\hline\end{array}$ | $\begin{array}{r}6\\-3\\\hline\end{array}$ | $\begin{array}{r}5\\-2\\\hline\end{array}$ |

$\begin{array}{r}5\\-5\\\hline\end{array}$

| $\begin{array}{r}7\\-4\\\hline\end{array}$ | $\begin{array}{r}3\\+5\\\hline\end{array}$ | $\begin{array}{r}0\\+4\\\hline\end{array}$ | $\begin{array}{r}7\\-5\\\hline\end{array}$ | $\begin{array}{r}2\\+3\\\hline\end{array}$ | $\begin{array}{r}5\\-3\\\hline\end{array}$ |

START

$\begin{array}{r}8\\-2\\\hline\end{array}$

| $\begin{array}{r}4\\+4\\\hline\end{array}$ | $\begin{array}{r}6\\-1\\\hline\end{array}$ | $\begin{array}{r}2\\+2\\\hline\end{array}$ | $\begin{array}{r}5\\+3\\\hline\end{array}$ |

© Houghton Mifflin Harcourt Publishing Company

Game Caterpillar Chase

▶ Using the Game

Materials number cube (labeled 1–6), 1 red connecting cube and 1 blue connecting cube, or other playing pieces

This activity gives children an opportunity to practice basic addition and subtraction facts. Partners take turns tossing the number cube and moving his or her playing piece that many spaces. The partner says the answer for the vertical addition or subtraction problem on the space on which he or she lands. The other partner then checks the answer. If it is correct, that player stays on the space. If the answer is incorrect, the player goes back to the space on which he or she started.

Partners take turns. The first partner to get to FINISH wins the game.

School-Home Letter available in English and Spanish in the *Standards Practice Book*, pp. P51–P52

The letter provides families with an overview of the math in the chapter, math vocabulary, an activity, and literature to read together.

Standards Practice

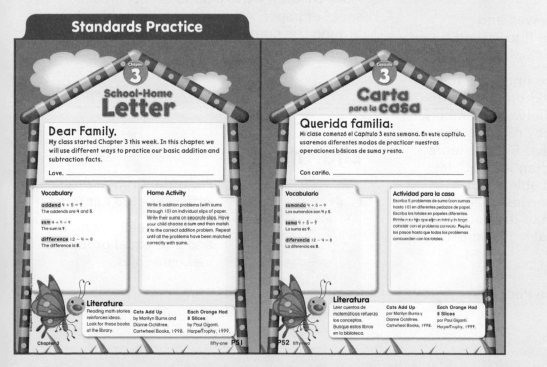

School-Home Letter

Dear Family,

My class started Chapter 3 this week. In this chapter, we will use different ways to practice our basic addition and subtraction facts.

Love, _____

Vocabulary

addend 4 + 5 = 9
The addends are 4 and 5.

sum 4 + 5 = 9
The sum is 9.

difference 12 − 4 = 8
The difference is 8.

Home Activity

Write 5 addition problems (with sums through 10) on individual slips of paper. Write their sums on separate slips. Have your child choose a sum and then match it to the correct addition problem. Repeat until all the problems have been matched correctly with sums.

Literature

Reading math stories reinforces ideas. Look for these books at the library.

Cats Add Up
by Marilyn Burns and Dianne Ochiltree.
Cartwheel Books, 1998.

Each Orange Had 8 Slices
by Paul Giganti.
HarperTrophy, 1999.

Chapter 3 fifty-one **P51**

Carta para la casa

Querida familia:

Mi clase comenzó el Capítulo 3 esta semana. En este capítulo, usaremos diferentes modos de practicar nuestras operaciones básicas de suma y resta.

Con cariño, _____

Vocabulario

sumando 4 + 5 = 9
Los sumandos son 4 y 5.

suma 4 + 5 = 9
La suma es 9.

diferencia 12 − 4 = 8
La diferencia es 8.

Actividad para la casa

Escriba 5 problemas de suma (con sumas hasta 10) en diferentes pedazos de papel. Escriba los totales en papeles diferentes. Pídale a su hijo que elija un total y lo haga coincidir con el problema correcto. Repita los pasos hasta que todos los problemas concuerden con los totales.

Literatura

Leer cuentos de matemáticos refuerza los conceptos. Busque estos libros en la biblioteca.

Cats Add Up
por Marilyn Burns y Dianne Ochiltree.
Cartwheel Books, 1998.

Each Orange Had 8 Slices
por Paul Giganti.
HarperTrophy, 1999.

P52 fifty-two

Use Doubles Facts

LESSON AT A GLANCE

Common Core Standard

Add and subtract within 20.
CC.2.OA.2 Fluently add and subtract within 20 using mental strategies. By end of Grade 2, know from memory all sums of two one-digit numbers.

Lesson Objective

Use doubles facts as a strategy for finding sums for near doubles facts.

Essential Question

How can you use doubles facts to find sums for near doubles facts?

Vocabulary sums

Materials MathBoard

Digital Path

- ☑ Animated Math Models
- 𝕄𝕄 HMH Mega Math
- i𝐓 iTools: Counters
- 🔵 eStudent Edition

COMMON CORE PROFESSIONAL DEVELOPMENT

About the Math

Why Teach This?

In this chapter, various strategies are reviewed and reinforced in order for children to achieve fluency with the basic facts.

In this lesson, children use doubles facts to find sums for near doubles facts. This strategy helps children develop their understanding of the relationships between numbers. For example, a child is able to solve 5 + 6 by recalling the doubles fact 5 + 5 = 10 and recognizing that 6 is one more than 5. So, the sum of 5 + 6 is one more than the doubles fact 5 + 5 = 10. Similarly, children are also able to solve 5 + 4 because they understand that 4 is one less than 5. As children become fluent in the application of the doubles fact strategy, they strengthen their mental math skills.

Professional Development Video Podcasts

Daily Routines

Common Core

SPIRAL REVIEW

Problem of the Day

eTransparency **3.1**

Number of the Day 256

Write a number that is greater than 256.
Write a number that is less than 256. Possible answers: 260; 156

Have children use symbols to compare 256 with the greater number. Then have them compare 256 with the lesser number. Possible answers: 256 < 260; 256 > 156 Have children explain how they used place value to compare the numbers.

Vocabulary Builder

Doubles

One at a time, read these facts aloud.

2 + 5 = 7; 5 + 5 = 10; 7 + 7 = 14; 9 + 0 = 9;

2 + 2 = 4; 7 + 3 = 10; 4 + 1 = 5; 8 + 8 = 16.

Ask children to raise their hands each time they hear a doubles fact.

Have children write a doubles fact on a sheet of paper. Ask them to draw a blue box around the numbers that are the same and a red box around the sum.

Literature

From the Grab-and-Go™ Differentiated Centers Kit

Children read the book and add equal groups to make doubles.

Doubles Fun on the Farm

Differentiated Instruction Activities

ELL Language Support
Kinesthetic / Small Group

Strategy: Draw

Materials paper, purple and red crayons

- Children can make drawings to review vocabulary and understand new concepts.

- Point out to children that in a doubles fact the numbers being added are the same. Give children this problem:

  Benji has 4 flowers. Mary has 4 flowers. How many flowers do they have in all?

- Have children make a drawing that shows Benji's flowers and Mary's flowers by drawing two groups in two rows. Have children use a different color for each person's flowers. Point out the one-to-one correspondence.

- Then have children write an addition sentence to show the number of flowers in all.

See **ELL** Activity Guide for leveled activities.

Enrich
Kinesthetic / Interpersonal Partners

Materials sets of Numeral Cards 2–9 (see *eTeacher Resources*)

- Have one child choose a card. Have the other child name the number 1 greater than or 1 less than that number.

- Have children use the numbers to write two addition problems. For example, with a 4-card and the number 5, children would write $4 + 5 = $ _____ and $5 + 4 = $ _____ .

- Each partner takes one of the problems. Then they each use two different doubles facts to find the sum of their problem in two ways.

$$5 + 4 = \underline{\qquad}$$
$$5 + 5 - 1 = 9$$
$$4 + 4 + 1 = 9$$

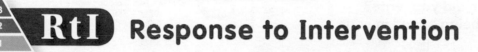

RtI Response to Intervention

Reteach Tier 1
Kinesthetic / Visual / Whole Class / Small Group

Materials red and blue connecting cubes

- Write $6 + 7 = $ _____ on the board. Say: **You can use $6 + 6 = 12$ to help find the sum of $6 + 7$.** Have children put cubes together to make two 6-cube trains of the same color. Have them say the doubles fact that the cubes represent.

- **Now change the model to show $6 + 7$. 7 is one more than 6.** Demonstrate adding one more cube of a different color to one of the 6-cube trains.

- **The cubes show $6 + 6 + 1$. Why is $6 + 6 + 1$ the same as $6 + 7$?** Have children use their cubes to explain their answer. Possible answer: because 7 has the same value as $6 + 1$

- Have a similar discussion to find the sum for $6 + 7$ using $7 + 7 - 1$. Demonstrate making two 7-cube trains and then breaking off one cube.

Tier 2
Kinesthetic / Visual / Small Group

Materials two-color counters

- Write $5 + 6$ on the board. Have children model the problem by placing 5 red counters in a row and 5 red counters and 1 yellow counter directly below the first row.

- **How can you describe the number of red counters in the two groups?** Both groups have 5 red counters.

- Below $5 + 6$, write $5 + 5 + 1$, using an arrow to show that 6 is written as $5 + 1$.

- Circle $5 + 5$. Have children use their two groups of red counters to find the sum. 10 Discuss that just as 6 is one more than 5, the sum of $5 + 6$ is one more than the sum of $5 + 5$.

- Write $10 + 1$ on the board below $5 + 5 + 1$, using an arrow to show that $5 + 5$ is written as 10. Then have children find the sum. 11

1 ENGAGE iTools
Online

Materials *iTools:* Counters

Access Prior Knowledge Use the *i*Tools counters to model doubles facts. For example, show two groups of 3 counters.

Have children tell how many counters there are in all. Repeat this activity with two groups of 2 counters and two groups of 4 counters.

2 TEACH and TALK  Animated
Online Math Models

▶ **Listen and Draw** REAL WORLD

Read the following problem aloud.

Nathan has 6 toy cars. Alisha gives him 6 more toy cars. How many toy cars does Nathan have now?

Then have children draw a picture on the page to represent the problem. You may wish to suggest that children draw simple shapes, such as circles or *X*s, to stand for toy cars.

- **Describe what you drew to show the problem.** Possible answer: I drew two groups of six toy cars.

- **What is the problem that you are solving?** how many toy cars Nathan has now

Have children use their drawings to write an addition sentence.

- **What addition sentence did you write? Describe the numbers being added in your number sentence.** 6 + 6 = 12. The numbers being added are the same.

- **What are some other doubles facts that you know?** Some possible answers: 1 + 1 = 2; 2 + 2 = 4; 3 + 3 = 6; 4 + 4 = 8; 5 + 5 = 10; 7 + 7 = 14; 8 + 8 = 16; 9 + 9 = 18

Use **Math Talk** to focus on children's understanding of why certain facts are called doubles facts.

COMMON CORE

CC.2.OA.2 Fluently add and subtract within 20 using mental strategies. By end of Grade 2, know from memory all sums of two one-digit numbers.

Name _____

Lesson **3.1**

Use Doubles Facts

COMMON CORE STANDARD CC.2.OA.2
Add and subtract within 20.

Essential Question How can you use doubles facts to find sums for near doubles facts?

Listen and Draw REAL WORLD

Draw a picture to show the problem. Then write an addition sentence for the problem. **Check children's drawings.**

6 (+) 6 (=) 12

__12__ toy cars

Math Talk: Possible answer: When you add two numbers that are the same, it is like doubling that number.

Math Talk
Explain why 4 + 4 = 8 is called a doubles fact.
MATHEMATICAL PRACTICES

FOR THE TEACHER • Read this problem and have children draw a picture for the problem. Nathan has 6 toy cars. Alisha gives him 6 more toy cars. How many toy cars does Nathan have now? After children write an addition sentence, have them name other doubles facts that they know.

Chapter 3

one hundred twenty-one **121**

Standards Practice 3.1

Common Core SPIRAL REVIEW

Name _____

Lesson **3.1**

Use Doubles Facts

COMMON CORE STANDARD CC.2.OA.2
Add and subtract within 20.

Write a doubles fact you can use to find the sum. Write the sum.

Doubles facts may vary. Check children's work.

1. 2 + 3 = __5__
___ + ___ = ___

2. 7 + 6 = __13__
___ + ___ = ___

3. 3 + 4 = __7__
___ + ___ = ___

4. 8 + 9 = __17__
___ + ___ = ___

5. 6 + 5 = __11__
___ + ___ = ___

6. 4 + 5 = __9__
___ + ___ = ___

PROBLEM SOLVING REAL WORLD

Solve. Write or draw to explain.

7. There are 6 ants on a log. Then 7 ants crawl onto the log. How many ants are on the log now?

__13__ ants

Chapter 3

fifty-three **P53**

Lesson Check (CC.2.OA.2)

★TEST PREP

1. What is the sum?

4 + 3 = ___

○ 3
○ 4
○ 6
● 7

2. What is the sum?

6 + 7 = ___

● 13
○ 12
○ 7
○ 6

Spiral Review (CC.2.OA.3, CC.2.NBT.1, CC.2.NBT.3, CC.2.NBT.4)

3. There are 451 children in Lia's school. Which of these numbers is greater than 451? (Lesson 2.11)

● 511
○ 415
○ 399
○ 154

4. What number is shown with these blocks? (Lesson 2.8)

○ 112
○ 142
● 152
○ 162

5. Which of these numbers has the digit 8 in the tens place? (Lesson 2.5)

○ 18
○ 278
● 483
○ 864

6. Which sum is an even number? (Lesson 1.2)

○ 2 + 3 = 5
○ 3 + 4 = 7
○ 4 + 5 = 9
● 6 + 6 = 12

P54 fifty-four

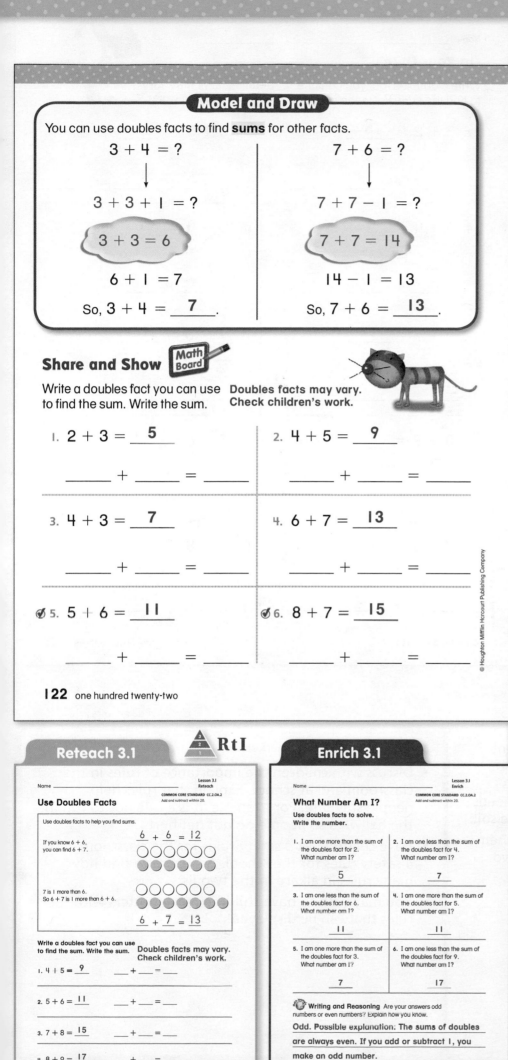

Model and Draw

You can use doubles facts to find **sums** for other facts.

$3 + 4 = ?$
↓
$3 + 3 + 1 = ?$

$3 + 3 = 6$

$6 + 1 = 7$

So, $3 + 4 = \underline{7}$.

$7 + 6 = ?$
↓
$7 + 7 - 1 = ?$

$7 + 7 = 14$

$14 - 1 = 13$

So, $7 + 6 = \underline{13}$.

Share and Show

Write a doubles fact you can use to find the sum. Write the sum.

Doubles facts may vary. Check children's work.

1. $2 + 3 = \underline{5}$

___ + ___ = ___

2. $4 + 5 = \underline{9}$

___ + ___ = ___

3. $4 + 3 = \underline{7}$

___ + ___ = ___

4. $6 + 7 = \underline{13}$

___ + ___ = ___

5. $5 + 6 = \underline{11}$

___ + ___ = ___

6. $8 + 7 = \underline{15}$

___ + ___ = ___

122 one hundred twenty-two

© Houghton Mifflin Harcourt Publishing Company

Model and Draw

Work through the model with children. Point out that they can use a doubles fact to find the sum of a number that has 1 more or 1 less than a doubles fact.

- **Why can 3 + 4 be written as 3 + 3 + 1?** Possible answer: 4 is the same as one more than 3.

- **Why can 7 + 6 be written as 7 + 7 − 1?** Possible answer: 6 is the same as one less than 7.

- **Can you write 3 + 4 as 4 + 4 − 1? Explain.** Yes; Possible answer: 3 is the same as one less than 4.

3 PRACTICE

Share and Show • Guided Practice

Exercises 1–6 connect to the learning model.

- **In Exercise 1, which doubles fact did you use? Explain your choice.** Possible answer: I used 2 + 2 = 4 because 2 is a number in the problem. Then I added one more because 3 is one more than 2.

Use Exercises 5 and 6 for **Quick Check**. Children should use their MathBoards to show their solutions to these exercises.

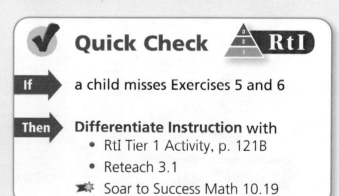

✓ **Quick Check** RtI

If a child misses Exercises 5 and 6

Then Differentiate Instruction with
- RtI Tier 1 Activity, p. 121B
- Reteach 3.1
- Soar to Success Math 10.19

⚠ COMMON ERRORS

Error Children may not understand when to add 1 or subtract 1 from the doubles fact.

Example In Exercise 3, children write $4 + 3 = 9$.

Springboard to Learning Have children write a doubles fact they can use to find the sum for a given problem. Then have them circle the number in the problem that is not in the doubles fact. Ask children if the number that they circled is 1 more or 1 less than each of the numbers being added in the doubles fact.

▶ On Your Own • Independent Practice

If children answer Exercises 5 and 6 correctly, assign Exercises 7–16.

Point out that children should write the sum on the line next to the given problem. On the lines below the problem, they should write the doubles fact that they used.

Go Deeper

Give children the doubles fact 5 + 5 = 10. Have them use this doubles fact to write two near doubles facts. 5 + 6 = 11; 5 + 4 = 9. Ask children to explain how they found their answers. Then have them repeat the activity for the doubles fact 4 + 4 = 8. 4 + 5 = 9; 4 + 3 = 7.

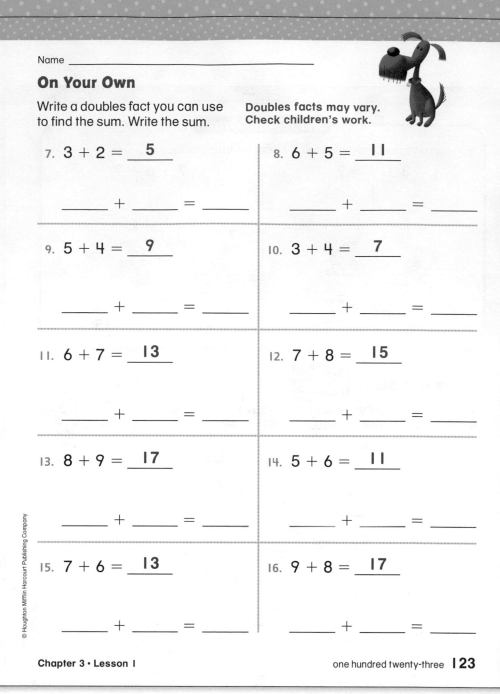

Name _____

On Your Own

Write a doubles fact you can use to find the sum. Write the sum.

Doubles facts may vary. Check children's work.

7. 3 + 2 = __5__

_____ + _____ = _____

8. 6 + 5 = __11__

_____ + _____ = _____

9. 5 + 4 = __9__

_____ + _____ = _____

10. 3 + 4 = __7__

_____ + _____ = _____

11. 6 + 7 = __13__

_____ + _____ = _____

12. 7 + 8 = __15__

_____ + _____ = _____

13. 8 + 9 = __17__

_____ + _____ = _____

14. 5 + 6 = __11__

_____ + _____ = _____

15. 7 + 6 = __13__

_____ + _____ = _____

16. 9 + 8 = __17__

_____ + _____ = _____

© Houghton Mifflin Harcourt Publishing Company

Chapter 3 • Lesson 1   one hundred twenty-three **123**

Cross-Curricular

SCIENCE

- Explain to children that living things have different needs. Animals and plants are living things with some of the same needs, such as water and air. Animals have other needs, such as food and shelter. The needs of plants also include light and nutrients from the soil.
- Have children name 6 animals and 5 plants. Ask them to find how many living things in all are in the two lists. 11 living things

SOCIAL STUDIES

Materials posterboard, markers

- Discuss with children the importance of rules in the classroom and at school. Explain that rules help people stay safe. For example, it is a rule not to run in the hallways so people do not get hurt.
- Have children list 3 safety rules for the classroom and 4 safety rules for the school. Ask them to find how many rules in all are in the two lists. 7 rules
- You may wish to have children make posters with the rules that can be displayed.

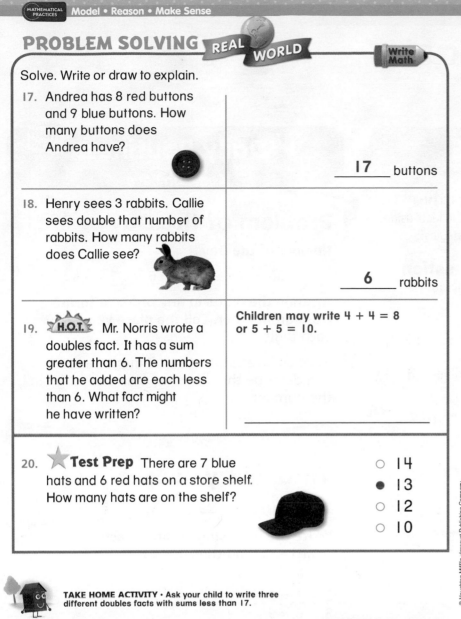

PROBLEM SOLVING — REAL WORLD

Write Math

Solve. Write or draw to explain.

17. Andrea has 8 red buttons and 9 blue buttons. How many buttons does Andrea have?

17 buttons

18. Henry sees 3 rabbits. Callie sees double that number of rabbits. How many rabbits does Callie see?

6 rabbits

19. H.O.T. Mr. Norris wrote a doubles fact. It has a sum greater than 6. The numbers that he added are each less than 6. What fact might he have written?

Children may write 4 + 4 = 8 or 5 + 5 = 10.

20. ★ **Test Prep** There are 7 blue hats and 6 red hats on a store shelf. How many hats are on the shelf?

○ 14
● 13
○ 12
○ 10

TAKE HOME ACTIVITY · Ask your child to write three different doubles facts with sums less than 17.

124 one hundred twenty-four

FOR MORE PRACTICE:
Standards Practice Book, pp. P53–P54

▶ **Problem Solving** MATHEMATICAL PRACTICES

Have children read Exercise 17. Ask them to describe how they will solve the problem.

H.O.T. Problem In Exercise 19, children use higher order thinking skills to find a doubles fact by using clues. If children need help starting, suggest that children make a list of doubles facts with addends less than 6.

★ Test Prep Coach

Test Prep Coach helps teachers to identify common errors that children can make.

In Exercise 20, if children selected:

- **14,** they used the doubles fact 7 + 7 = 14 but forgot to subtract 1.
- **12,** they used the doubles fact 6 + 6 = 12 but forgot to add 1.
- **10,** they did not add correctly.

4 SUMMARIZE MATHEMATICAL PRACTICES

Essential Question

How can you use doubles facts to find sums for near doubles facts? Possible answer: If I know the sum of a doubles fact, I find the sum for a near doubles fact by comparing the numbers being added and deciding if I need to add 1 or subtract 1 from the sum of the doubles fact.

Math Journal

Draw or write to show two ways to use a doubles fact to find 6 + 7.

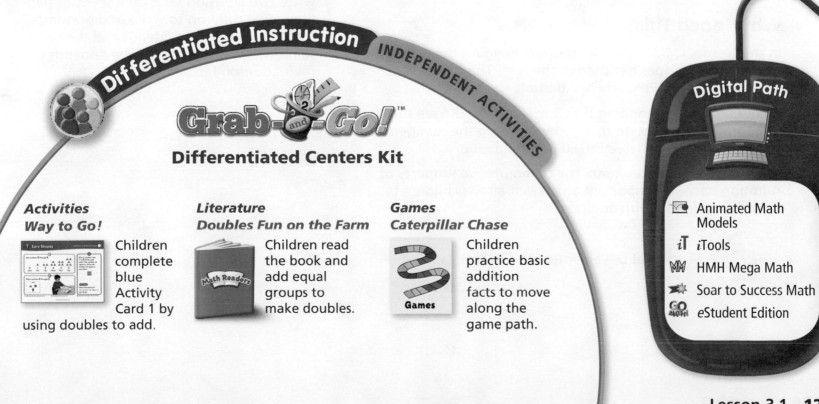

Differentiated Instruction — INDEPENDENT ACTIVITIES

Grab-and-Go!

Differentiated Centers Kit

Activities Way to Go!
Children complete blue Activity Card 1 by using doubles to add.

Literature Doubles Fun on the Farm
Children read the book and add equal groups to make doubles.

Games Caterpillar Chase
Children practice basic addition facts to move along the game path.

Digital Path

- Animated Math Models
- iT iTools
- HMH Mega Math
- Soar to Success Math
- eStudent Edition

Practice Addition Facts

LESSON AT A GLANCE

Common Core Standard

Add and subtract within 20.
CC.2.OA.2 Fluently add and subtract within 20 using mental strategies. By end of Grade 2, know from memory all sums of two one-digit numbers.

Lesson Objective

Recall sums for basic facts using properties and strategies.

Essential Question

What are some ways to remember sums?

Vocabulary addends

Materials MathBoard

Digital Path

☑ **Animated Math Models**   *iT* **iTools: Number Charts**

〽 **HMH Mega Math**   **eStudent Edition**

COMMON CORE
PROFESSIONAL DEVELOPMENT

About the Math

Why Teach This?

In this lesson, children will learn that changing the order of the addends does not change the sum. This is known as the Commutative Property of Addition.

At this age, understanding that 3 + 4 and 4 + 3 have the same sum helps to build fluency by reducing the number of facts that children need to commit to memory.

As children advance in math, the Commutative Property of Addition becomes important again as it allows children to simplify equations with addition.

PODCASTING

Professional Development Video Podcasts

Daily Routines

Math Board

Common Core

SPIRAL REVIEW

Problem of the Day

eTransparency 3.2

Number of the Day

9 5 6

Arrange the digits in any order to form a 3-digit number. Tell the place value of each digit.

Have children share their 3-digit numbers and describe the place value of each digit in the number.

Vocabulary Builder

Addends

Write the following addition facts on the board and read them aloud.

1 + 8 = 9
2 + 7 = 9
3 + 6 = 9

Have volunteers come to the board and circle the addends in each fact. Then have children write two addition facts on a sheet of paper. Challenge children to write addition facts that have different addends and the same sum. Ask children to circle the addends in their addition facts.

Differentiated Instruction Activities

ELL Language Support 🕐 Kinesthetic Small Group

Strategy: Model Concepts

Materials two-color counters

- Children may understand concepts, story problems, and vocabulary if they are illustrated or modeled.

- Have children show 5 red counters and add 7 yellow counters. **What addition facts does your model show?** 5 + 7 = 12 and 7 + 5 = 12

- Discuss with children how you can add numbers in any order.

See **ELL** Activity Guide for leveled activities.

Enrich 🕐 Visual, Verbal / Linguistic Partners

Materials Secret Code Cards 1–9 (front and back) (see *eTeacher Resources*)

- Have children work in pairs. One child shows the numeral side of a card and the dot side of another card. The other child writes an addition sentence using the numbers that the cards show as the addends.

- Ask children to describe how they found the sum. Then have children switch tasks and repeat the activity for a different pair of cards.

RtI Response to Intervention

Reteach Tier 1 🕐 Kinesthetic / Visual Whole Class / Small Group

Materials connecting cubes in two colors

- Write *4 + 8* on the board. Have children make a connecting cube train to show this problem. Tell them to use two colors of cubes, one for each number.

- Have children explain how their cube train shows 4 + 8 = 12. Possible answer: I have 4 cubes of one color and 8 cubes of another color. There are 12 cubes in all.

- Have children turn the cube train around.

- **What addition fact does your cube train show now?** 8 + 4 = 12 Write *8 + 4* on the board.

- Have children add to check their work. Have children describe how the cube train changed and how it stayed the same when they turned it around.

Tier 2 🕐 Visual / Kinesthetic Small Group

Materials connecting cubes in two colors

- Write *7 + 2* on the board. Model how to make a cube train to show this problem with a 7-cube train of one color and a 2-cube train of another color. Discuss how the cubes show the problem.

- Then have children make the same model. Ask them to connect the two trains.

- Ask: **What is the sum of 7 + 2? How can you tell from your train?** 9; My train is 9 cubes long.

- Have children turn the cube train around. **What is the sum of 2 + 7? How can you tell from your train?** 9; My train is 9 cubes long.

- Point out to children that the sum stayed the same even though the order of the numbers changed.

1 ENGAGE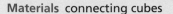

Materials connecting cubes

Access Prior Knowledge Use connecting cubes to illustrate the Commutative Property of Addition. Show children a train of 3 red cubes and 4 blue cubes.

- **What addition fact is shown?** 3 + 4 = 7

Then flip the train so that it shows 4 blue cubes and 3 red cubes.

- **What addition fact is shown now?** 4 + 3 = 7
- **How are these two cube trains alike?** They have the same number of blue cubes and red cubes.
- **How are they different?** In the first train, the red cubes are first and the blue cubes are next. In the second train, the blue cubes are first and the red cubes are next.

Repeat for 2 + 7 = 9 and 7 + 2 = 9.

2 TEACH and TALK
GO Online · Animated Math Models

▶ Listen and Draw REAL WORLD

Read the problem and ask a volunteer to retell the problem in his or her own words.

On Monday, Tony recycled 3 cans and 6 bottles. How many containers did he recycle?

Have children draw a picture and write a number sentence for the problem in the top box. Then ask these questions.

- **How does your drawing show the problem?** Answers will vary, but should show an understanding of representing addition with a drawing.

- **How did you decide whether to write an addition or a subtraction sentence?** Possible answer: I wrote an addition sentence to show that I was combining the numbers of objects.

Then read the following problem. Have children draw a picture and write a number sentence for the problem in the bottom box.

On Tuesday, Tony recycled 6 cans and 3 bottles. How many containers did he recycle?

Use **Math Talk** to focus on children's understanding that changing the order of the addends does not change the sum.

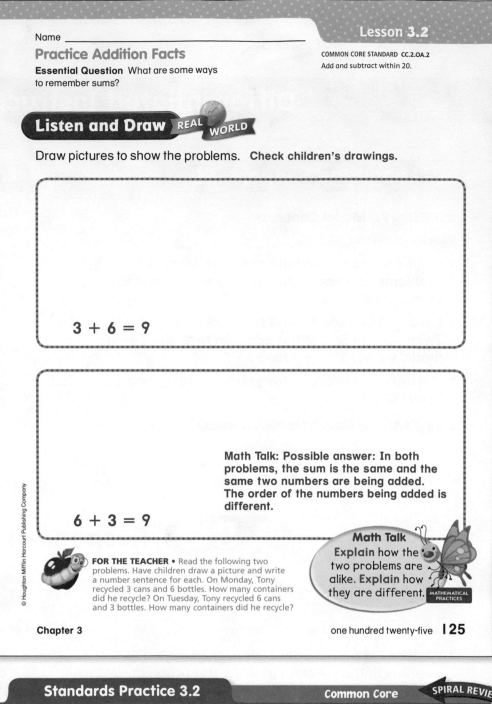

COMMON CORE CC.2.OA.2 Fluently add and subtract within 20 using mental strategies. By end of Grade 2, know from memory all sums of two one-digit numbers.

Name _____

Lesson 3.2

Practice Addition Facts

COMMON CORE STANDARD CC.2.OA.2
Add and subtract within 20.

Essential Question What are some ways to remember sums?

Listen and Draw REAL WORLD

Draw pictures to show the problems.   Check children's drawings.

3 + 6 = 9

6 + 3 = 9

Math Talk: Possible answer: In both problems, the sum is the same and the same two numbers are being added. The order of the numbers being added is different.

FOR THE TEACHER · Read the following two problems. Have children draw a picture and write a number sentence for each. On Monday, Tony recycled 3 cans and 6 bottles. How many containers did he recycle? On Tuesday, Tony recycled 6 cans and 3 bottles. How many containers did he recycle?

Math Talk **Explain** how the two problems are alike. **Explain** how they are different. MATHEMATICAL PRACTICES

Chapter 3

one hundred twenty-five **125**

Standards Practice 3.2
Common Core · SPIRAL REVIEW

Name _____

Lesson 3.2

Practice Addition Facts

COMMON CORE STANDARD CC.2.OA.2
Add and subtract within 20.

Write the sums.

1. 9 + 1 = **10**
   1 + 9 = **10**
2. 7 + 6 = **13**
   6 + 7 = **13**
3. 8 + 0 = **8**
   5 + 0 = **5**
4. **16** = 7 + 9
   16 = 9 + 7
5. 4 + 4 = **8**
   4 + 5 = **9**
6. 9 + 9 = **18**
   9 + 8 = **17**
7. 8 + 8 = **16**
   8 + 7 = **15**
8. 2 + 2 = **4**
   2 + 3 = **5**
9. **9** = 6 + 3
   9 = 3 + 6
10. 6 + 6 = **12**
    6 + 7 = **13**
11. **7** = 0 + 7
    9 = 0 + 9
12. 5 + 5 = **10**
    5 + 6 = **11**
13. 8 + 5 = **13**
    5 + 8 = **13**
14. 8 + 2 = **10**
    2 + 8 = **10**
15. 7 + 4 = **11**
    4 + 7 = **11**

PROBLEM SOLVING REAL WORLD

Solve. Write or draw to explain.

16. Jason has 7 puzzles. Quincy has the same number of puzzles as Jason. How many puzzles do they have altogether?

14 puzzles

Chapter 3

fifty-five **P55**

Lesson Check (CC.2.OA.2)

⭐ TEST PREP

1. What is the sum?
   8 + 7 = ___
   - ● 15
   - ○ 14
   - ○ 12
   - ○ 11

2. What is the sum?
   2 + 9 = ___
   - ○ 7
   - ● 11
   - ○ 12
   - ○ 13

Spiral Review (CC.2.NBT.2, CC.2.NBT.3, CC.2.NBT.4, CC.2.NBT.8)

3. Which is another way to describe 43? (Lesson 1.4)
   - ● 40 + 3
   - ○ 30 + 4
   - ○ 4 + 3
   - ○ 40 + 30

4. Which number is 100 more than 276? (Lesson 2.9)
   - ○ 176
   - ○ 286
   - ● 376
   - ○ 672

5. Which group of numbers shows counting by tens? (Lesson 1.8)
   - ○ 10, 11, 12, 13, 14
   - ○ 15, 20, 25, 30, 35
   - ● 20, 30, 40, 50, 60
   - ○ 60, 59, 58, 57, 56

6. Which of the following is true? (Lesson 2.12)
   - ○ 127 > 142
   - ○ 142 < 127
   - ○ 127 = 142
   - ● 127 < 142

P56 fifty-six

Model and Draw

These are some ways to remember facts.

You can count on 1, 2, or 3.

$6 + 1 = \underline{7}$

$6 + 2 = \underline{8}$

$6 + 3 = \underline{9}$

Changing the order of the **addends** does not change the sum.

$\underline{8} = 2 + 6$

$\underline{8} = 6 + 2$

Share and Show

Write the sums.

1. $2 + 2 = \underline{4}$
   $2 + 3 = \underline{5}$

2. $5 + 0 = \underline{5}$
   $2 + 0 = \underline{2}$

3. $3 + 8 = \underline{11}$
   $8 + 3 = \underline{11}$

4. $\underline{8} = 4 + 4$
   $\underline{7} = 4 + 3$

5. $5 + 7 = \underline{12}$
   $7 + 5 = \underline{12}$

6. $\underline{14} = 7 + 7$
   $\underline{15} = 7 + 8$

7. $\underline{10} = 3 + 7$
   $\underline{10} = 7 + 3$

◎ 8. $9 + 3 = \underline{12}$
   $3 + 9 = \underline{12}$

◎ 9. $\underline{12} = 6 + 6$
   $\underline{11} = 6 + 5$

126 one hundred twenty-six

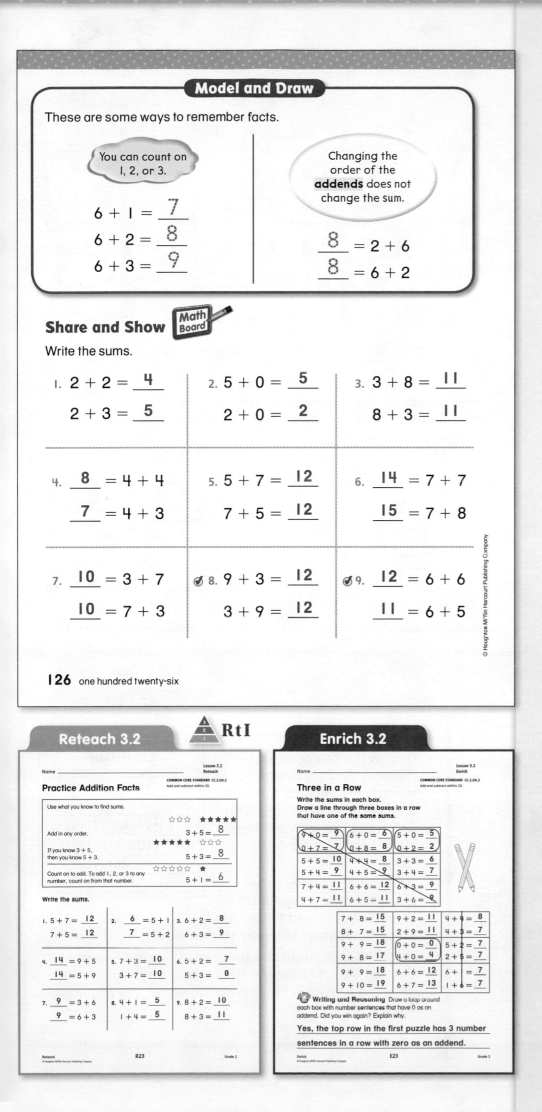

Reteach 3.2

Name _____

Lesson 3.2
Reteach

COMMON CORE STANDARD CC.2.OA.2
Add and subtract within 20.

Practice Addition Facts

Use what you know to find sums.

☆☆☆ ★★★★★
Add in any order.
$3 + 5 = \underline{8}$

★★★★★ ☆☆☆
If you know $3 + 5$,
then you know $5 + 3$.
$5 + 3 = \underline{8}$

☆☆☆☆☆ ★
Count on to add. To add 1, 2, or 3 to any number, count on from that number.
$5 + 1 = \underline{6}$

Write the sums.

1. $5 + 7 = \underline{12}$
   $7 + 5 = \underline{12}$

2. $\underline{6} = 5 + 1$
   $\underline{7} = 5 + 2$

3. $6 + 2 = \underline{8}$
   $6 + 3 = \underline{9}$

4. $\underline{14} = 9 + 5$
   $\underline{14} = 5 + 9$

5. $7 + 3 = \underline{10}$
   $3 + 7 = \underline{10}$

6. $5 + 2 = \underline{7}$
   $5 + 3 = \underline{8}$

7. $\underline{9} = 3 + 6$
   $\underline{9} = 6 + 3$

8. $4 + 1 = \underline{5}$
   $1 + 4 = \underline{5}$

9. $8 + 2 = \underline{10}$
   $8 + 3 = \underline{11}$

Reteach R23 Grade 2
© Houghton Mifflin Harcourt Publishing Company

Enrich 3.2

Name _____

Lesson 3.2
Enrich

COMMON CORE STANDARD CC.2.OA.2
Add and subtract within 20.

Three in a Row

Write the sums in each box.
Draw a line through three boxes in a row that have one of the same sums.

$9 + 0 = \underline{9}$ $0 + 7 = \underline{7}$	$6 + 0 = \underline{6}$ $0 + 8 = \underline{8}$	$5 + 0 = \underline{5}$ $0 + 2 = \underline{2}$
$5 + 5 = \underline{10}$ $5 + 4 = \underline{9}$	$4 + 4 = \underline{8}$ $4 + 5 = \underline{9}$	$3 + 3 = \underline{6}$ $3 + 4 = \underline{7}$
$7 + 4 = \underline{11}$ $4 + 7 = \underline{11}$	$6 + 6 = \underline{12}$ $6 + 5 = \underline{11}$	$6 + 3 = \underline{9}$ $3 + 6 = \underline{9}$

$7 + 8 = \underline{15}$ $8 + 7 = \underline{15}$	$9 + 2 = \underline{11}$ $2 + 9 = \underline{11}$	$4 + 4 = \underline{8}$ $4 + 3 = \underline{7}$
$9 + 9 = \underline{18}$ $9 + 8 = \underline{17}$	$0 + 0 = \underline{0}$ $4 + 0 = \underline{4}$	$5 + 2 = \underline{7}$ $2 + 5 = \underline{7}$
$9 + 9 = \underline{18}$ $9 + 10 = \underline{19}$	$6 + 6 = \underline{12}$ $6 + 7 = \underline{13}$	$6 + \underline{\ } = \underline{7}$ $1 + 6 = \underline{7}$

Writing and Reasoning Draw a loop around each box with number sentences that have 0 as an addend. Did you win again? Explain why.

Yes, the top row in the first puzzle has 3 number sentences in a row with zero as an addend.

Enrich E23 Grade 2
© Houghton Mifflin Harcourt Publishing Company

Model and Draw

Work through the strategies and examples with children. For the first strategy, model counting on 1, 2, or 3. Then direct children's attention to the related facts.

- **When the addends in two facts are the same, why are the sums the same?**
  Possible answer: The same two numbers are being added together. Changing their order does not change the sum.

(3) PRACTICE

Share and Show • Guided Practice

Exercises 1–9 connect to the learning model. Children can use the two modeled strategies to solve these problems.

- **Look at Exercise 2. Describe what happens when zero is added to a number.**
  Possible answer: When you add zero to a number, the sum is that number.

Have children describe strategies they can use when finding sums in the exercises.

Use Exercises 8 and 9 for Quick Check. Children should use their MathBoards to show their solutions to these exercises.

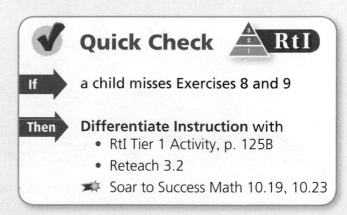

✓ Quick Check · RtI

If a child misses Exercises 8 and 9

Then Differentiate Instruction with
- RtI Tier 1 Activity, p. 125B
- Reteach 3.2
- Soar to Success Math 10.19, 10.23

⚠ COMMON ERRORS

Error Children may not recognize the sum when it appears on the left of the equal sign.

Example In Exercise 4, children do not write the sum before the equal sign.

Springboard to Learning Remind children that number sentences can be written in different ways. Talk about how both sides of the equal sign must have the same value. Then have children write pairs of facts such as $4 + 3 = 7$ and $7 = 4 + 3$.

If children answer Exercises 8 and 9 correctly, assign Exercises 10–25.

For Exercises 22–25, children use the table provided to determine which addition fact to write. Discuss what an addition table is and how it is set up. Be sure children understand where the sum for a given pair of addends is shown in the table.

- **How do you know which addition fact to write for Exercise 22?** Possible answer: There is a blue box around the fact, so I look for the blue box in the addition table and write the fact for the addends of that box. The fact for Exercise 22 is 3 + 1 = 4, or 1 + 3 = 4.

Go Deeper

Write some addition problems (without sums) on the board. Have children identify a strategy they can use to find each sum. They may name one of the strategies discussed in this lesson or the previous lesson, or they may describe another strategy. To encourage them to communicate mathematical ideas, have them discuss or draw a diagram to explain how the strategy helps them find the sum.

9 + 7	2 + 9	5 + 4
3 + 7	6 + 5	6 + 8

Name _____

On Your Own

Write the sums.

10. $7 + 1 = \underline{8}$
    $1 + 7 = \underline{8}$

11. $\underline{4} = 4 + 0$
    $\underline{9} = 9 + 0$

12. $5 + 5 = \underline{10}$
    $5 + 4 = \underline{9}$

13. $8 + 2 = \underline{10}$
    $2 + 8 = \underline{10}$

14. $3 + 3 = \underline{6}$
    $3 + 4 = \underline{7}$

15. $7 + 8 = \underline{15}$
    $8 + 7 = \underline{15}$

16. $\underline{5} = 4 + 1$
    $\underline{5} = 1 + 4$

17. $0 + 7 = \underline{7}$
    $0 + 6 = \underline{6}$

18. $8 + 8 = \underline{16}$
    $8 + 9 = \underline{17}$

19. $5 + 3 = \underline{8}$
    $3 + 5 = \underline{8}$

20. $\underline{18} = 9 + 9$
    $\underline{17} = 9 + 8$

21. $6 + 7 = \underline{13}$
    $7 + 6 = \underline{13}$

Find the addends for each shaded box in the addition table. Write the facts for the shaded boxes. **Order of addends may vary.**

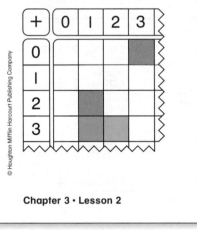

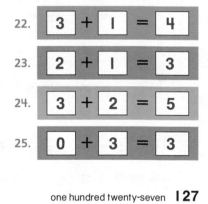

22. $3 + 1 = 4$

23. $2 + 1 = 3$

24. $3 + 2 = 5$

25. $0 + 3 = 3$

Cross-Curricular   SCIENCE

- Discuss with children the properties of flowering plants, including color. As the children name the colors of various flowering plants, write this information on the board.

- Have children write addition sentences to show various combinations of flowers. For example, for the flowers above, they might write 4 + 5 = 9.
- Have children explain a strategy they can use to find the sum.

SOCIAL STUDIES

Materials calendar

- Discuss the calendar with children. Review how to identify the days of the week and the dates for those days. Ask questions such as "How many Mondays are in the month?"

October						
Sunday	Monday	Tuesday	Wednesday	Thursday	Friday	Saturday
						1
2	3	4	5	6	7	8
9	10	11	12	13	14	15
16	17	18	19	20	21	22
23	24	25	26	27	28	29
30	31					

- Have children solve this problem. **Mimi plays soccer every Tuesday and Friday. How many times does she play this month?**
- Have children count the number of Tuesdays and the number of Fridays in the current month. Then have them write a number sentence for the problem and solve.

PROGRAM SOLVING — REAL WORLD

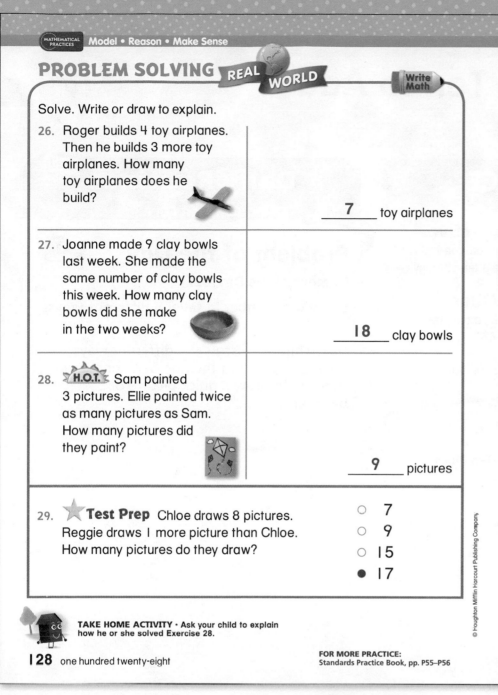

Solve. Write or draw to explain.

26. Roger builds 4 toy airplanes. Then he builds 3 more toy airplanes. How many toy airplanes does he build?

_____7_____ toy airplanes

27. Joanne made 9 clay bowls last week. She made the same number of clay bowls this week. How many clay bowls did she make in the two weeks?

_____18_____ clay bowls

28. H.O.T. Sam painted 3 pictures. Ellie painted twice as many pictures as Sam. How many pictures did they paint?

_____9_____ pictures

29. Test Prep Chloe draws 8 pictures. Reggie draws 1 more picture than Chloe. How many pictures do they draw?

○ 7
○ 9
○ 15
● 17

TAKE HOME ACTIVITY · Ask your child to explain how he or she solved Exercise 28.

128 one hundred twenty-eight

FOR MORE PRACTICE:
Standards Practice Book, pp. P55–P56

▶ **Problem Solving** (MATHEMATICAL PRACTICES)

Have children read Exercise 26. Ask them to describe how they will solve the problem.

Unlock the Problem Children may choose to use a doubles fact to help them solve Exercise 26.

H.O.T. Problem Exercise 28 is a non-routine, multistep problem. Discuss with children that the word *twice* means double. Have children describe all the steps they will use to solve.

Test Prep Coach

Test Prep Coach helps teachers to identify common errors that children can make. In Exercise 29, if children selected:

• **7,** they subtracted numbers in the problem.
• **9,** they added the numbers in the problem.
• **15,** they used 1 fewer picture for Reggie.

4 SUMMARIZE (MATHEMATICAL PRACTICES)

Essential Question

What are some ways to remember sums?
Possible answer: I can count on by 1, 2, or 3; change the order of the addends; or use doubles facts. I also know that any number plus 0 equals that number.

Math Journal

Write or draw to explain a way to find each sum: 6 + 7, 8 + 4, 2 + 9.

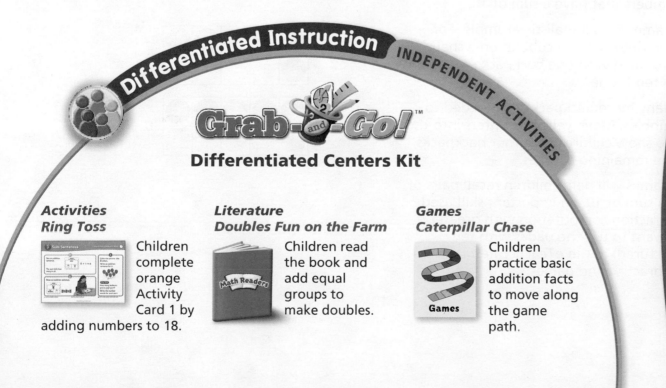

Differentiated Instruction — INDEPENDENT ACTIVITIES

Grab-and-Go!
Differentiated Centers Kit

Activities
Ring Toss
Children complete orange Activity Card 1 by adding numbers to 18.

Literature
Doubles Fun on the Farm
Children read the book and add equal groups to make doubles.

Games
Caterpillar Chase
Children practice basic addition facts to move along the game path.

Digital Path

☑ Animated Math Models
iT iTools
MM HMH Mega Math
★ Soar to Success Math
GO eStudent Edition

Lesson 3.2 128

Algebra • Make a Ten to Add

LESSON AT A GLANCE

Common Core Standard
Add and subtract within 20.
CC.2.OA.2 Fluently add and subtract within 20 using mental strategies. By end of Grade 2, know from memory all sums of two one-digit numbers.

Lesson Objective
Recall sums for addition facts using the make a ten strategy.

Essential Question
How is the make a ten strategy used to find sums?

Materials MathBoard

Digital Path

☑ **Animated Math Models**

𝖶𝖬 **HMH Mega Math**

𝑖𝐓 *i*Tools: Base-Ten Blocks

𝐆𝐎 *e*Student Edition

Daily Routines

SPIRAL REVIEW

Common Core

Problem of the Day

eTransparency **3.3**

Number of the Day 327

Show the number in several different ways.
Check children's work.

Have children discuss the different ways they can represent the number. For example, they might draw a quick picture or use base-ten blocks.

COMMON CORE
MATHEMATICAL PRACTICES 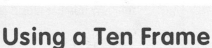 **Using a Ten Frame**

A ten frame is a spatial organizer for children. It may be used to develop mental images or representations for combinations of numbers that have a sum of 10.

Introduce the ten frame using a realistic example. For example, tell children there are ten cubbies on a shelf. Six of the cubbies are filled with one backpack each. Show six red counters in a ten frame.

Ask children how many more backpacks are needed to fill the rest of the cubbies. Move yellow counters into the four empty spaces to show children that four backpacks are needed to fill the remaining cubbies.

Working with ten frames will help children recall pairs of numbers that have a sum of 10, an important skill used in addition and subtraction computation with greater numbers. You may want to use the pages with ten frames (with dots pictured) in the *eTeacher Resources* as flashcards for extra practice and games.

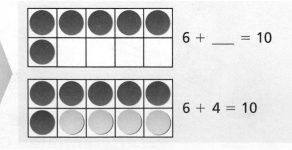

$6 + \_\_ = 10$

$6 + 4 = 10$

Differentiated Instruction Activities

ELL Language Support | Kinesthetic / Small Group

Strategy: Model Concepts

Materials two-color counters, Ten Frames (see *eTeacher Resources*)

- Children may understand the make a ten strategy when it is modeled.

- Place 9 counters in the ten frame. Explain that 1 more counter is needed to make 10.

- Discuss how to make 10 in different ways.

- Guide children in using the counters in the ten frame to make 10. Have children write the number sentence for each way they make 10.

See **ELL** Activity Guide for leveled activities.

Enrich | Visual / Kinesthetic / Individual / Partners

Materials 2 sets of Secret Code Cards 1–10, *Count On Me* Game Board (see *eTeacher Resources*), color paper

- Players fold their game board and use the addition side. Set 1 of the cards is placed above the game board. Player 2 holds the other set.

- Player 1 selects a card from Set 1 and places it in the box to the left of the + sign. Player 2 selects a card from Set 1 and places it in the box following the + sign.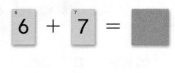

- Player 2 selects the card or cards from Set 2 to show the sum in the box following the = sign. He or she uses a piece of color paper to cover the sum.

- Player 1 says the total. Player 2 checks the answer. Players continue, switching roles.

RtI Response to Intervention

Reteach Tier 1 | Visual / Kinesthetic / Whole Class / Small Group

Materials blue and red paper clips, egg carton with 10 compartments

- Write $8 + 7 =$ _____ . Ask children to gather 8 red paper clips and 7 blue paper clips. Have children place each red paper clip into a single compartment in the egg carton. Then have them place 1 blue paper clip in each remaining compartment.

- Ask: **How many paper clips are in the carton?** 10 paper clips **How many paper clips are left over?** 5 paper clips **What is 10 + 5?** 15 Guide children to see that 15 is the number of red and blue clips in all, so $8 + 7 = 15$.

Tier 2 | Visual / Kinesthetic / Small Group

Materials Ten Frames (see *eTeachers Resources*), two-color counters

- Have a volunteer fill the ten frame using 10 red counters.

- Remove 2 counters from the ten frame. Have a volunteer use yellow counters to fill the ten frame. Write $8 + 2 = 10$. Flip over 2 red counters so there are 4 yellow counters in the ten frame. Ask: **What addition fact does this show?** 6 + 4 = 10, or 4 + 6 = 10

- Write $7 + 4 =$ _____ on the board. Have a volunteer put 7 red counters in the ten frame. Then have the child take 4 yellow counters and fill the ten frame. Ask: **How many extra counters do you have?** 1 counter **How many counters are there in all?** 11 counters Write $7 + 4 = 11$.

1 ENGAGE

Materials two-color counters, Ten Frames
(see *eTeacher Resources*)

Access Prior Knowledge Group children in pairs. Give each pair 10 counters and a ten frame.

- **How can you use a ten frame to show 3 + 7?** Possible answer: I use 3 red counters and 7 yellow counters to show 10 in a ten frame.

- **What is a different combination of yellow and red counters that shows a sum of 10?** Answers will vary. Possible answers: 2 + 8, 1 + 9, 5 + 5, 6 + 4

2 TEACH and TALK  Animated Math Models

▶ **Listen and Draw** REAL WORLD

Read the following problem.

There are 6 dog bones and 4 dog biscuits. How many dog treats are there?

Have children point to the ten frame that is a model for the problem. Ask children to write the addition sentence for the model.
6 + 4 = 10

- **What if there were 5 bones and 5 biscuits? Point to the ten frame. Write an addition sentence for this model.** 5 + 5 = 10

- **Point to the ten frame that is a model for 8 bones and 2 biscuits. Write an addition sentence for this model.** 8 + 2 = 10

- **What if there were 9 bones and 1 biscuit? Write an addition sentence for this model.** 9 + 1 = 10

- **Which is a model for 7 bones and 3 biscuits? Write an addition sentence for this model.** 7 + 3 = 10

- **How are these facts alike?** They all have a sum of 10. **How are they different?** They have different addends.

Use **Math Talk** to focus on children's understanding of the make a ten strategy.

CC.2.OA.2 Fluently add and subtract within 20 using mental strategies. By end of Grade 2, know from memory all sums of two one-digit numbers.

Name _____

Lesson 3.3

Algebra • Make a Ten to Add

COMMON CORE STANDARD CC.2.OA.2
Add and subtract within 20.

Essential Question How is the make a ten strategy used to find sums?

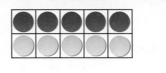
Listen and Draw  REAL WORLD

Write the fact below the ten frame when you hear the problem that matches the model.

$$5 + 5 = 10$$

$$6 + 4 = 10$$

$$7 + 3 = 10$$

$$8 + 2 = 10$$

$$9 + 1 = 10$$

Math Talk: Some possible patterns: the sums are all 10; as the first addend increases by 1, the second addend decreases by 1.

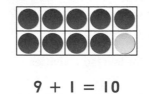
FOR THE TEACHER • Read the following problem. There are 6 dog bones and 4 dog biscuits. How many dog treats are there? Have children find the ten frame that models the problem and write the addition sentence. Repeat by revising the story for each addition fact represented by the other ten frames.

Math Talk
Describe a pattern you see in these make a ten facts.

MATHEMATICAL PRACTICES

Chapter 3

one hundred twenty-nine **129**

Standards Practice 3.3

Common Core

SPIRAL REVIEW

Name _____

Lesson 3.3

Algebra • Make a Ten to Add

COMMON CORE STANDARD CC.2.OA.2
Add and subtract within 20.

Show how you can make a ten to find the sum.
Write the sum.

1. 9 + 7 = __16__
   10 + __6__ = __16__

2. 8 + 5 = __13__
   10 + __3__ = __13__

3. 8 + 6 = __14__
   10 + __4__ = __14__

4. 3 + 9 = __12__
   10 + __2__ = __12__

5. 8 + 7 = __15__
   10 + __5__ = __15__

6. 6 + 5 = __11__
   10 + __1__ = __11__

7. 7 + 6 = __13__
   10 + __3__ = __13__

8. 5 + 9 = __14__
   10 + __4__ = __14__

PROBLEM SOLVING REAL WORLD

Solve. Write or draw to explain.

9. There are 9 children on the bus. Then 8 more children get on the bus. How many children are on the bus now?

__17__ children

Chapter 3

fifty-seven **P57**

Lesson Check (CC.2.OA.2)

★TEST PREP

1. Which has the same sum as 8 + 7?
   ○ 10 + 3
   ○ 10 + 4
   ● 10 + 5
   ○ 10 + 6

2. Which has the same sum as 7 + 5?
   ○ 10 + 1
   ● 10 + 2
   ○ 10 + 3
   ○ 10 + 4

Spiral Review (CC.2.OA.3, CC.2.NBT.3)

3. Which number can be written as 200 + 10 + 7? (Lesson 2.7)
   ○ 207
   ○ 210
   ● 217
   ○ 271

4. Which of these is an odd number? (Lesson 1.1)
   ○ 2
   ○ 4
   ○ 6
   ● 7

5. What is the value of the underlined digit? (Lesson 1.3)
   6**5**
   ● 60
   ○ 50
   ○ 10
   ○ 6

6. Which is another way to write the number 47? (Lesson 1.5)
   ○ 40 + 70
   ○ seventy-four
   ● 4 tens 7 ones
   ○ 4 + 7

P58 fifty-eight

Model and Draw

$7 + 5 = ?$

You need to add 3 to 7 to make a ten.
Break apart 5 as 3 and 2.

$7 + 5$
$7 + 3 + 2$
$10 + 2 = \underline{12}$

So, $7 + 5 = \underline{12}$.

Share and Show

Show how you can make a ten to find the sum.
Write the sum.

1. $8 + 3 = \underline{11}$
   2 1
   $10 + \underline{1} = \underline{11}$

2. $2 + 9 = \underline{11}$
   1 1
   $10 + \underline{1} = \underline{11}$

3. $8 + 5 = \underline{13}$
   $10 + \underline{3} = \underline{13}$

4. $4 + 7 = \underline{11}$
   $10 + \underline{1} = \underline{11}$

5. $3 + 9 = \underline{12}$
   $10 + \underline{2} = \underline{12}$

6. $7 + 6 = \underline{13}$
   $10 + \underline{3} = \underline{13}$

130 one hundred thirty

▶ **Model and Draw**

Work through the model with children.

- **Why is 5 broken apart as 3 and 2 to solve?**
  Possible answer: A 3 is needed to make a ten with 7.

- **Why is 10 + 2 the last step in the cloud?**
  Possible answer: 5 was broken apart as 3 and 2. The 3 was added to 7 to make 10, so the 2 still needs to be added to find the sum.

Be sure children realize this strategy makes sense only when the sum is 10 or greater.

MATHEMATICAL PRACTICES How does finding tens help in addition problems?

③ PRACTICE

▶ **Share and Show** • Guided Practice

Exercises 1–6 connect to the learning model.

- **Do you think it is easier to break apart the greater addend or the lesser addend? Explain.** Possible answer: the lesser addend; It is easier to look at the greater addend and decide how to break apart the other addend to make a 10.

Use Exercises 5 and 6 for **Quick Check**. Children should use their Math Boards to show their solutions to these exercises.

Quick Check

If	a child misses Exercises 5 and 6
Then	**Differentiate Instruction** with • RtI Tier 1 Activity, p. 129B • Reteach 3.3 • Soar to Success Math 10.20

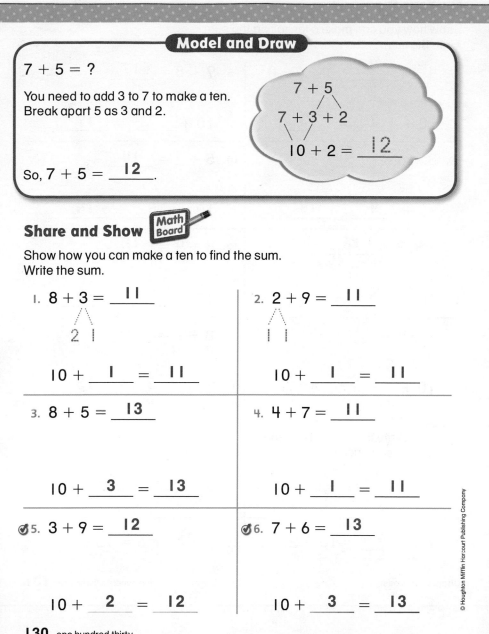

Name _____

Algebra • Make a Ten to Add

COMMON CORE STANDARD CC.2.OA.2
Add and subtract within 20.

$8 + 5 = \underline{?}$

Step 1 Start with the greater addend. Break apart the other addend to make a ten.

8 + 5

Step 2 You need to add 2 to 8 to make a ten. So, break apart 5 as 2 and 3.

$8 + 2 = 10$

Step 3 Add on the rest to the 10. $10 + \underline{3} = 13$

Step 4 Write the sum. $8 + 5 = \underline{13}$

Show how you can make a ten to find the sum. Write the sum.

1. $7 + 6 = \underline{13}$
   3 3
   $10 + \underline{3} = \underline{13}$

2. $9 + 2 = \underline{11}$
   1 1
   $10 + \underline{1} = \underline{11}$

3. $4 + 8 = \underline{12}$
   2 2
   $10 + \underline{2} = \underline{12}$

4. $5 + 9 = \underline{14}$
   $10 + \underline{4} = \underline{14}$

5. $8 + 6 = \underline{14}$
   $10 + \underline{4} = \underline{14}$

6. $4 + 9 = \underline{13}$
   $10 + \underline{3} = \underline{13}$

Reteach R24 Grade 2

Name _____

Lesson 3.3
Enrich

Make a Ten Again

COMMON CORE STANDARD CC.2.OA.2
Add and subtract within 20.

Write the fact. Circle ten animals. Then write the make a ten fact to find the total number of animals.

$8 + 5 = ?$
$10 + 3 = 13$

$9 + 5 = ?$
$10 + 4 = 14$

$8 + 8 = ?$
$10 + 6 = 16$

$5 + 7 = ?$
$10 + 2 = 12$

Writing and Reasoning How did you decide which make a ten fact to use? Explain.

Possible answer: After I circled each group of ten, I looked at the number of animals left. Then I added that number to 10.

Enrich E24 Grade 2

! **COMMON ERRORS**

Error Children may break the addend into a combination that does not make a ten, and then continue on as if it did make a ten.

Example $7 + 8 =$
4 4

$10 + 4 = 14$

Springboard to Learning Have children use a ten frame to help them remember facts with sums of 10.

On Your Own • Independent Practice

If children answer Exercises 5 and 6 correctly, assign Exercises 7–18.

H.O.T. Problems In Exercises 15–18, children use higher order thinking skills as they find missing addends in addition sentences. Encourage children to use the make a ten strategy to find each missing addend.

• **How can you use the make a ten strategy to help you find the missing addend in Exercise 15?** Possible answer: I look at 9 + 6. 9 is the greater addend, so I break apart 6 as 1 and 5 because 5 is the given addend on the right. I put 1 with 9 to make 10, so 9 + 6 = 10 + 5.

Go Deeper

MATHEMATICAL PRACTICES

Explain to children that the make a ten strategy is most effective when making ten with the greater addend.

Some children may find it easier to always break apart the second addend in an addition sentence. Discuss with children how changing the order of addends does not change the sum. They can rewrite an addition sentence so that the greater addend is the first addend and the addend that they need to break apart is the second addend.

Name _____

On Your Own

Show how you can make a ten to find the sum. Write the sum.

7. 4 + 9 = __13__
3 1

10 + __3__ = 13

8. 9 + 8 = __17__
1 7

10 + __7__ = 17

9. 8 + 6 = __14__

10 + __4__ = 14

10. 5 + 9 = __14__

10 + __4__ = 14

11. 7 + 9 = __16__

10 + __6__ = 16

12. 8 + 4 = __12__

10 + __2__ = 12

13. 9 + 9 = __18__

10 + __8__ = 18

14. 8 + 7 = __15__

10 + __5__ = 15

H.O.T. Write the missing addend that makes the number sentence true.

15. 9 + 6 = __10__ + 5

16. 8 + 5 = 10 + __3__

17. 7 + __5__ = 10 + 2

18. __8__ + 6 = 10 + 4

PROBLEM SOLVING REAL WORLD   Write Math

Solve. Write or draw to explain.

19. There are 9 red bicycles at the store. There are 6 yellow bicycles at the store. How many bicycles are at the store?

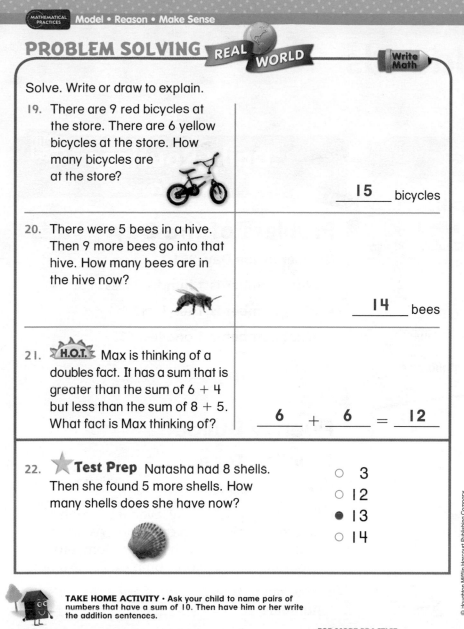

15 bicycles

20. There were 5 bees in a hive. Then 9 more bees go into that hive. How many bees are in the hive now?

14 bees

21. **H.O.T.** Max is thinking of a doubles fact. It has a sum that is greater than the sum of 6 + 4 but less than the sum of 8 + 5. What fact is Max thinking of?

6 + **6** = **12**

22. ⭐ **Test Prep** Natasha had 8 shells. Then she found 5 more shells. How many shells does she have now?

- ○ 3
- ○ 12
- ● 13
- ○ 14

🏠 **TAKE HOME ACTIVITY** · Ask your child to name pairs of numbers that have a sum of 10. Then have him or her write the addition sentences.

132 one hundred thirty-two

© Houghton Mifflin Harcourt Publishing Company

FOR MORE PRACTICE:
Standards Practice Book, pp. P57–P58

▶ **Problem Solving** MATHEMATICAL PRACTICES

Have children read Exercise 19. Ask them to describe how they will solve the problem.

Unlock the Problem To solve Exercise 19, children may use the make a ten strategy.

H.O.T. Problem To solve Exercise 21, children use clues to find a doubles fact.

- **What do you know about the sum of this doubles fact?** It is between 10 and 13.

⭐ **Test Prep Coach**

Test Prep Coach helps teachers to identify common errors that children can make.

In Exercise 22, if children selected:
- **3,** they subtracted the numbers.
- **12,** they added incorrectly.
- **14,** they added incorrectly.

4 SUMMARIZE MATHEMATICAL PRACTICES

Essential Question

How is the make a ten strategy used to find sums? Possible answer: You break apart the lesser addend to make a ten. You add 10 plus the remaining part of the addend to find the sum.

Math Journal

Describe how you can use the make a ten strategy to find the sum of 7 + 9.

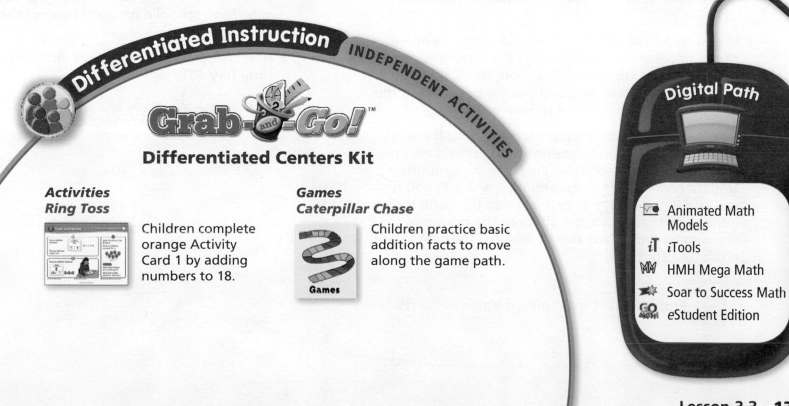

Differentiated Instruction INDEPENDENT ACTIVITIES

Grab-and-Go!
Differentiated Centers Kit

Activities
Ring Toss

Children complete orange Activity Card 1 by adding numbers to 18.

Games
Caterpillar Chase

Children practice basic addition facts to move along the game path.

Digital Path

- ☑ Animated Math Models
- *i*T *i*Tools
- MM HMH Mega Math
- ⭐ Soar to Success Math
- GO eStudent Edition

Algebra • Add 3 Addends

LESSON AT A GLANCE

Common Core Standard

Add and subtract within 20.
CC.2.OA.2 Fluently add and subtract within 20 using mental strategies. By end of Grade 2, know from memory all sums of two one-digit numbers.

Also CC.2.NBT.5

Lesson Objective

Find sums of three addends by applying the Commutative and Associative Properties of Addition.

Essential Question

How do you add three numbers?

Materials MathBoard

Digital Path

☑ Animated Math Models
𝖬𝖬 HMH Mega Math
iT *i*Tools: Counters
📚 *e*Student Edition

COMMON CORE
PROFESSIONAL DEVELOPMENT **About the Math**

Why Teach This?

In this chapter, children use two important addition properties.

* In Lesson 3.2 they learned that changing the order of the addends does not change the sum. This is the Commutative Property of Addition. Understanding this property helps children build fluency by reducing the number of facts they need to memorize.

* In this lesson, children learn that changing the way addends are grouped does not change the sum. This is known as the Associative Property of Addition. Understanding that when adding 3 + 2 + 6, you first can add 3 + 2, or 3 + 6, or 2 + 6 and then add the third addend to that sum, gives children the option of finding the sum by using facts they know and the strategies that work best for them.

PODCASTING
📱 **Professional Development Video Podcasts**

SPIRAL REVIEW

Problem of the Day

eTransparency 3.4

Number of the Day 381

* **What number is 1 hundred less?** 281
* **What number is 1 ten less?** 371
* **What number is 1 one less?** 380

Fluency Builder

Counting Tape

EVERY DAY **COUNTS**®

Materials Counting Tape

Continue to update daily, even if you don't take time for discussion questions. As often as possible, ask two or three questions, either straightforward or more complex. For example:

* **How many tens and ones are in today's number?**
* **What day of school will it be in 10 more school days? In 9 more days? In 11 more days?**
* **What day of school was it 10 school days ago? Nine school days ago? Eleven school days ago?**
* **How many more school days until Day 30? Until Day 40?**

23 24 25 26 27 28 29 30 31

Differentiated Instruction Activities

ELL Language Support
Verbal / Linguistic
Whole Class / Small Group

Strategy: Model Concepts

Materials connecting cubes in three colors

- Children may understand concepts, story problems, and vocabulary if they are illustrated or modeled.

- Write this problem on the board and then read it aloud.

  Luis has 4 books. Carla has 6 books. Manuela has 3 books. How many books do they have in all?

- Have children model the problem and then discuss different ways they can put the cubes together to solve the problem. 13 books

See **ELL** Activity Guide for leveled activities.

Enrich
Visual / Linguistic
Individual / Partners

Materials three sets of Numeral Cards 1–9 (see *eTeacher Resources*)

- Shuffle the numeral cards and place them facedown. Have each child take three cards and add the numbers.

- The child with the greater total gets one point. The first child to get 10 points wins.

- Have partners check each other's work and discuss how they grouped the numbers to add. Have them repeat the activity with other numbers.

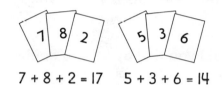

$$7 + 8 + 2 = 17 \qquad 5 + 3 + 6 = 14$$

RtI Response to Intervention

Reteach Tier 1
Visual / Kinesthetic
Whole Class / Small Group

Materials connecting cubes in three colors

- Write this number sentence on the board.

  $$2 + 7 + 3 = \underline{\hspace{1cm}}$$

- Have three children use cubes to model the three addends in the number sentence. Ask the first two children to put their cubes together and name the sum. 9 Write the sum on the board. Have the third child add the cubes and name the sum. 12 Write the sum on the board.

- Have children change positions and repeat the activity. Ask: **Does the sum change when you change the order of the addends?** no

Tier 2
Visual / Kinesthetic
Small Group

Materials connecting cubes in three colors

- Write this problem on the board.
  John has 4 stickers. Maria has 2 stickers. Rachel has 5 stickers. How many stickers do they have in all?

- Read the problem together. Have children model the three groups of stickers using three colors of cubes.

- **If you add the 4 cubes and 2 cubes together first, how many cubes is this?** 6 cubes **Then add the 5 cubes to the 6 cubes. What does this total show?** 5 + 6 = 11; they have 11 stickers in all.

① ENGAGE

Materials Addition Fact Cards (see *eTeacher Resources*)

Access Prior Knowledge Review addition basic facts by showing children the addition fact cards and having them name the sums. Have children discuss some of the strategies they use to find the sums.

- **What strategy did you use to find the sum for 9 + 7?** Possible answer: I used a make a ten fact: 9 + 7 = 9 + 1 + 6 = 10 + 6 = 16, so 9 + 7 = 16.

② TEACH and TALK GO Online Animated Math Models

▶ **Listen and Draw**

Read the directions aloud with children. After children have recorded the sum of each pair of addends, have them share their answers and discuss the strategies used.

- **Were there sums that you found more quickly than others? Explain.** Possible answer: I found the sum of 1 and 4 quickly because I know that 5 is one more than 4.

- **Which sums did you find by using a doubles fact?** Possible answer: I used a doubles fact to find the sums of 3 + 3 and 5 + 4.

- **Name a different fact that has a sum of 8.** Possible answers: 0 + 8 = 8; 1 + 7 = 8; 3 + 5 = 8; 4 + 4 = 8

Use **Math Talk** to focus on children's understanding of different strategies they can use to add.

Name _____ Lesson **3.4**

Algebra • Add 3 Addends
COMMON CORE STANDARD CC.2.OA.2
Add and subtract within 20.

Essential Question How do you add three numbers?

Listen and Draw

Write the sum of each pair of addends.

Math Talk: Possible answer: I know that 5 + 5 = 10, so I subtracted 1 to get 9.

FOR THE TEACHER • After children have recorded the sum of each pair of addends, have them share their answers and discuss the strategies used.

Math Talk
Describe how you found the sum of 5 and 4.
MATHEMATICAL PRACTICES

© Houghton Mifflin Harcourt Publishing Company

Chapter 3   one hundred thirty-three **133**

Standards Practice 3.4   **Common Core**   SPIRAL REVIEW

Name _____   Lesson **3.4**

Algebra • Add 3 Addends
COMMON CORE STANDARD CC.2.OA.2
Add and subtract within 20.

Solve two ways. Circle the two addends you add first.
Circled addends may vary.

1. 2 + 3 + 7 = __12__   2 + 3 + 7 = __12__

2. 5 + 3 + 3 = __11__   5 + 3 + 3 = __11__

3. 4 + 5 + 4 = __13__   4 + 5 + 4 = __13__

4. 4 + 4 + 4 = __12__   4 + 4 + 4 = __12__

5.
   5   5
   4   4
+ 5 + 5
 14   14

6.
   6   6
   3   3
+ 4 + 4
 13   13

PROBLEM SOLVING REAL WORLD

Choose a way to solve. Write or draw to explain.

7. Amber has 2 red crayons, 5 blue crayons, and 4 yellow crayons. How many crayons does she have in all?

__11__ crayons

Chapter 3   fifty-nine **P59**

Lesson Check (CC.2.OA.2)

1. What is the sum of 2 + 4 + 6?
   - ○ 6
   - ○ 8
   - ○ 10
   - ● 12

2. What is the sum of 5 + 4 + 2?
   - ● 11
   - ○ 9
   - ○ 7
   - ○ 6

Spiral Review (CC.2.NBT.1a, CC.2.NBT.1b, CC.2.NBT.3, CC.2.NBT.4, CC.2.NBT.8)

3. Which of the following is true? (Lesson 2.12)
   - ○ 264 < 246
   - ● 688 > 648
   - ○ 234 = 233
   - ○ 825 < 725

4. Which number can be written as 4 tens 2 ones? (Lesson 1.6)
   - ○ 12
   - ○ 14
   - ○ 24
   - ● 42

5. Which number has the same value as 50 tens? (Lesson 2.1)
   - ○ 5
   - ○ 50
   - ● 500
   - ○ 505

6. What is the next number in the pattern? (Lesson 2.10)
   420, 520, 620, 720, ▮
   - ● 820
   - ○ 850
   - ○ 920
   - ○ 980

P60 sixty

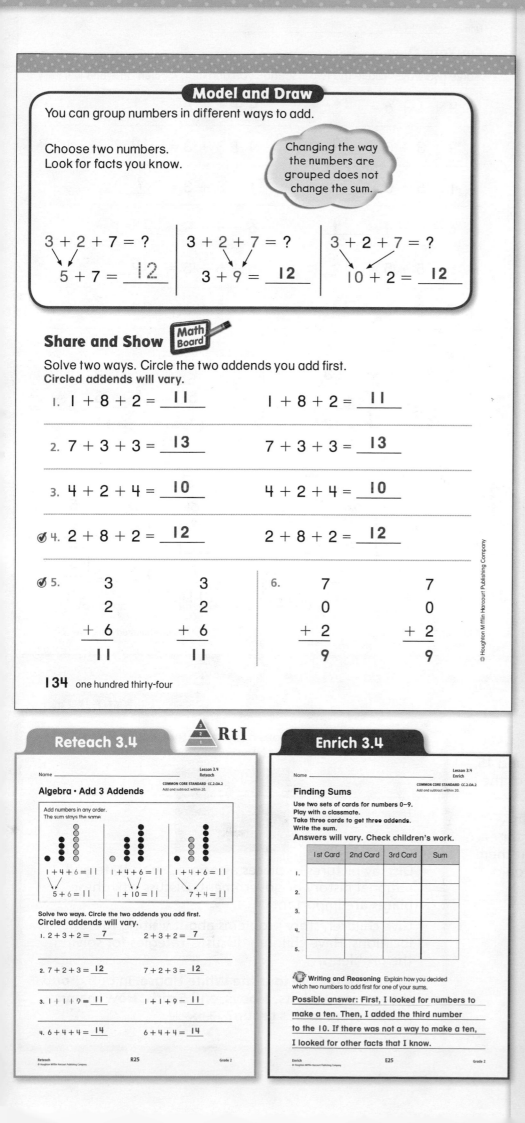

Model and Draw

You can group numbers in different ways to add.

Choose two numbers.
Look for facts you know.

Changing the way the numbers are grouped does not change the sum.

$3 + 2 + 7 = ?$
$5 + 7 = \underline{12}$

$3 + 2 + 7 = ?$
$3 + 9 = \underline{12}$

$3 + 2 + 7 = ?$
$10 + 2 = \underline{12}$

Share and Show

Solve two ways. Circle the two addends you add first.
Circled addends will vary.

1. $1 + 8 + 2 = \underline{11}$ $1 + 8 + 2 = \underline{11}$

2. $7 + 3 + 3 = \underline{13}$ $7 + 3 + 3 = \underline{13}$

3. $4 + 2 + 4 = \underline{10}$ $4 + 2 + 4 = \underline{10}$

4. $2 + 8 + 2 = \underline{12}$ $2 + 8 + 2 = \underline{12}$

5.
$$\begin{array}{r} 3 \\ 2 \\ + 6 \\ \hline 11 \end{array} \qquad \begin{array}{r} 3 \\ 2 \\ + 6 \\ \hline 11 \end{array}$$

6.
$$\begin{array}{r} 7 \\ 0 \\ + 2 \\ \hline 9 \end{array} \qquad \begin{array}{r} 7 \\ 0 \\ + 2 \\ \hline 9 \end{array}$$

134 one hundred thirty-four

Reteach 3.4

Name _____

Lesson 3.4
Reteach

COMMON CORE STANDARD CC.2.OA.2
Add and subtract within 20.

Algebra • Add 3 Addends

Add numbers in any order.
The sum stays the same.

$1 + 4 + 6 = 11$ $1 + 4 + 6 = 11$ $1 + 4 + 6 = 11$
$5 + 6 = 11$ $1 + 10 = 11$ $7 + 4 = 11$

Solve two ways. Circle the two addends you add first.
Circled addends will vary.

1. $2 + 3 + 2 = \underline{7}$ $2 + 3 + 2 = \underline{7}$

2. $7 + 2 + 3 = \underline{12}$ $7 + 2 + 3 = \underline{12}$

3. $1 + 1 + 9 = \underline{11}$ $1 + 1 + 9 = \underline{11}$

4. $6 + 4 + 4 = \underline{14}$ $6 + 4 + 4 = \underline{14}$

Reteach
© Houghton Mifflin Harcourt Publishing Company
R25
Grade 2

Enrich 3.4

Name _____

Lesson 3.4
Enrich

COMMON CORE STANDARD CC.2.OA.2
Add and subtract within 20.

Finding Sums

Use two sets of cards for numbers 0–9.
Play with a classmate.
Take three cards to get three addends.
Write the sum.
Answers will vary. Check children's work.

	1st Card	2nd Card	3rd Card	Sum
1.				
2.				
3.				
4.				
5.				

Writing and Reasoning Explain how you decided which two numbers to add first for one of your sums.

Possible answer: First, I looked for numbers to make a ten. Then, I added the third number to the 10. If there was not a way to make a ten, I looked for other facts that I know.

Enrich
© Houghton Mifflin Harcourt Publishing Company
E25
Grade 2

Model and Draw

MATHEMATICAL PRACTICES

Work through the model with children.

- **What is different about the three ways?** Different numbers are grouped together in the first step of solving the problem. **What is the same?** The sum is the same.

- **Why is the sum the same?** The same three numbers are being added each time. Changing the way the addends are grouped does not change the sum.

3 PRACTICE

Share and Show • Guided Practice

Exercises 1–6 connect to the learning model.

- **In Exercise 1, which addends did you group first for the two different ways?** Possible answer: For the first way, I grouped 1 and 8 and got 9, and then I added on 2 for a sum of 11. For the second way, I grouped 8 and 2 and got 10 and then added on 1 for a sum of 11.

- **How does solving in two ways help you know that your answer is correct?** Possible answer: If I get the same sum both ways, then my answer is probably correct.

Use Exercises 4 and 5 for **Quick Check**. Children should use their MathBoards to show their solutions to these exercises.

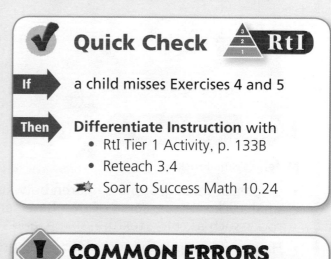

Quick Check RtI

If a child misses Exercises 4 and 5

Then **Differentiate Instruction** with
- RtI Tier 1 Activity, p. 133B
- Reteach 3.4
- Soar to Success Math 10.24

⚠ COMMON ERRORS

Error Children may find the sum for two addends and forget to add the third addend.

Example $2 + 8 + 2 = 10$

Springboard to Learning After children circle the two addends they add first, have them write the sum of these addends below the problem. Encourage them to draw arrows pointing from this sum to the two addends. Then they can see that they need to add the third addend to the sum they wrote.

Lesson 3.4   **134**

▶ On Your Own • Independent Practice

If children answer Exercises 4 and 5 correctly, assign Exercises 7–18.

H.O.T. Problems For Exercises 15–18, children use higher order thinking skills as they find a missing addend for an addition problem that is written in vertical format.

- **How did you find the missing addend in Exercise 15?** Possible answer: First I found the sum of 5 + 5, which is 10. Then I thought "10 plus what number is 14?" 10 + 4 = 14, so the missing addend is 4.

Go Deeper

MATHEMATICAL PRACTICES

Write the following problem on the board.

$$5 + \underline{\hspace{1cm}} + \underline{\hspace{1cm}} = 11$$

Challenge children to complete the addition sentence in as many ways as they can. Record their answers on the board. Then discuss patterns they see in the problems.

$5 + 0 + 6 = 11$
$5 + 1 + 5 = 11$
$5 + 2 + 4 = 11$
$5 + 3 + 3 = 11$
$5 + 4 + 2 = 11$
$5 + 5 + 1 = 11$
$5 + 6 + 0 = 11$

On Your Own

Solve two ways. Circle the two addends you add first. **Circled addends will vary.**

7. $4 + 1 + 6 = \underline{11}$ $4 + 1 + 6 = \underline{11}$

8. $4 + 3 + 3 = \underline{10}$ $4 + 3 + 3 = \underline{10}$

9. $1 + 5 + 3 = \underline{9}$ $1 + 5 + 3 = \underline{9}$

10. $6 + 4 + 4 = \underline{14}$ $6 + 4 + 4 = \underline{14}$

11. $5 + 5 + 5 = \underline{15}$ $5 + 5 + 5 = \underline{15}$

12. $7 + 0 + 6 = \underline{13}$ $7 + 0 + 6 = \underline{13}$

13.
```
  5        5
  3        3
+ 4      + 4
----     ----
 12       12
```

14.
```
  4        4
  2        2
+ 5      + 5
----     ----
 11       11
```

H.O.T. Write the missing addend.

15.
```
   5
   5
+ [4]
----
  14
```

16.
```
   4
 [4]
+  4
----
  12
```

17.
```
   3
 [1]
+  7
----
  11
```

18.
```
   5
   3
+ [5]
----
  13
```

Chapter 3 • Lesson 4   one hundred thirty-five **135**

© Houghton Mifflin Harcourt Publishing Company

Cross-Curricular

SCIENCE

Materials small rocks

- Give each small group of children between 10 and 15 small rocks. Discuss some of the characteristics of the rocks, such as color, texture, shape, and size.
- Have children put the rocks into three groups in different ways and write an addition sentence for each way. For example, if they have 13 rocks and put them in one group of 5 and two groups of 4, they would write the addition sentence 5 + 4 + 4 = 13.

SOCIAL STUDIES

Materials pictures of various national historical locations, such as the White House, Statue of Liberty, and Independence Hall

- Display pictures of places associated with state and national history or government. Discuss why these places are important.
- Give children story problems about visiting these locations. Have children discuss strategies for solving the problems.

   Groups of people tour the White House. In one group there were 3 adults, 5 boys, and 5 girls. How many people were in this group? 13 people

---

PROBLEM SOLVING — REAL WORLD

Write Math

Choose a way to solve.
Write or draw to explain.

19. Beth eats 4 green grapes. Lin eats 3 red grapes and 6 purple grapes. How many grapes do they eat?

_13_ grapes

20. There are 5 green grapes and 4 red grapes in a bowl. Eli puts 4 more red grapes in the bowl. How many grapes are in the bowl now?

_13_ grapes

21. **H.O.T.** Nick, Alex, and Sophia eat 15 raisins in all. Nick and Alex each eat 4 raisins. How many raisins does Sophia eat?

_7_ raisins

22. ⭐ **Test Prep** Mrs. Morgan has 2 red apples, 7 yellow apples, and 2 green apples. How many apples does she have?

○ 4
○ 9
○ 10
● 11

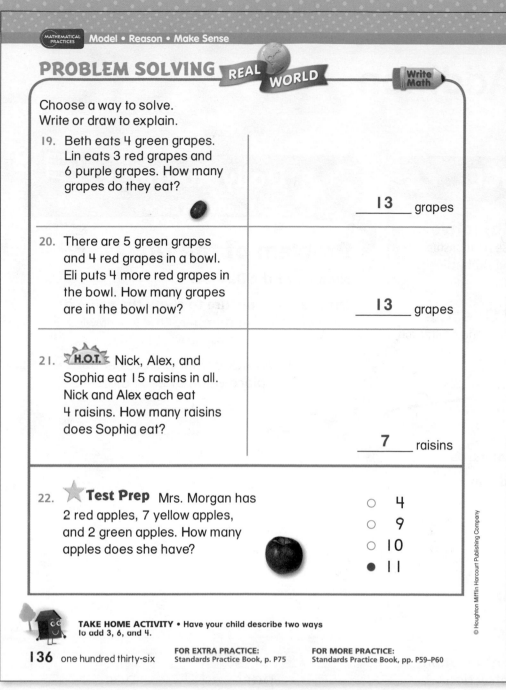

TAKE HOME ACTIVITY • Have your child describe two ways to add 3, 6, and 4.

136 one hundred thirty-six

FOR EXTRA PRACTICE: Standards Practice Book, p. P75

FOR MORE PRACTICE: Standards Practice Book, pp. P59–P60

▶ Problem Solving

Have children read Exercise 19. Ask them to describe how they will solve the problem.

Unlock the Problem A key to solving Exercise 19 is realizing that it is an addition problem with three addends.

H.O.T. Problem For Exercise 21, children find a missing addend in an addition word problem. Have children explain how they got their answers. Guide a discussion about the different ways children chose to solve the problem.

⭐ Test Prep Coach

Test Prep Coach helps teachers to identify common errors that children can make.

In Exercise 22, if children selected:
• **4,** they found the sum of 2 and 2.
• **9,** they found the sum of 2 and 7.
• **10,** they added incorrectly.

4 SUMMARIZE

Essential Question

How do you add three numbers? Possible answer: You add any two addends first and then add the third addend to that sum.

Math Journal

Write or draw to explain two ways you can find the sum of $3 + 4 + 5$.

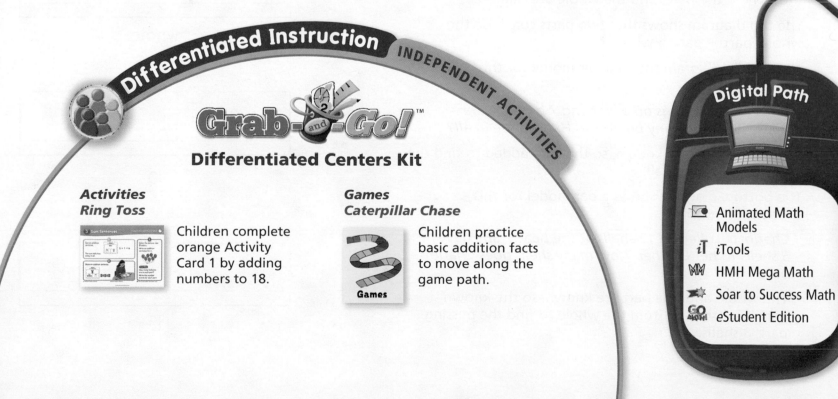

Differentiated Instruction — INDEPENDENT ACTIVITIES

Grab-and-Go! Differentiated Centers Kit

**Activities
Ring Toss**

Children complete orange Activity Card 1 by adding numbers to 18.

**Games
Caterpillar Chase**

Children practice basic addition facts to move along the game path.

Digital Path

- 📺 Animated Math Models
- iT iTools
- MM HMH Mega Math
- ⭐ Soar to Success Math
- GO Math eStudent Edition

Algebra • Relate Addition and Subtraction

LESSON AT A GLANCE

Common Core Standard
Add and subtract within 20.
CC.2.OA.2 Fluently add and subtract within 20 using mental strategies. By end of Grade 2, know from memory all sums of two one-digit numbers.

Vocabulary **differences**

Materials MathBoard

Lesson Objective
Use the inverse relationship of addition and subtraction to recall basic facts.

Essential Question
How are addition and subtraction related?

Digital Path

- Animated Math Models
- HMH Mega Math
- *iT* iTools: Counters
- eStudent Edition

Daily Routines
Common Core

Problem of the Day
eTransparency 3.5

Number of the Day 247

Draw a quick picture to show the value of each digit in the number. Children's drawings should show 2 hundreds, 4 tens, and 7 ones.

Have children share their pictures and identify the place value of each digit.

COMMON CORE MATHEMATICAL PRACTICES

Using Bar Models

A bar model is a visual tool used to organize information in a problem. A bar model for addition or subtraction shows how the parts and the whole are related.

The top diagram shows that two parts comprise the whole: part + part = whole.

The middle diagram shows a bar model for this addition problem.

Hudson sees 3 bugs on a leaf and 7 bugs on the sidewalk. How many bugs does Hudson see in all?

- The two parts are known, so they are added to find the whole: 10 bugs in all.

The bottom diagram shows a bar model for this subtraction problem.

Charlotte collected 13 shells at the beach. She gave 5 shells to her brother. How many shells does Charlotte have now?

- The whole and one part are known, so the known part is subtracted from the whole to find the missing part: 8 shells.

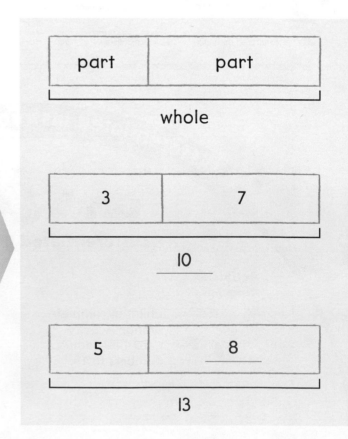

Differentiated Instruction Activities

ELL Language Support
🕐 | Visual
Small Group

Strategy: Identify Relationships

- Children understand language by making connections between words and their experiences.

- Ask children what they think *related* means when you talk about related facts.

- Show children two related facts. Tell them that the facts are related.

- Have children identify the relationships between the facts.

$$6 + 5 = 11$$
$$11 - 5 = 6$$

- Explain to children that there are addition facts that are related to subtraction facts. These related addition facts can help children find the difference for a subtraction fact. Have children write other related facts.

See **ELL** Activity Guide for leveled activities.

Enrich
🕐 | Visual
Individual / Partners

Materials index cards

- Have children use the numbers 1 to 18 to write a subtraction sentence on an index card, with the difference left blank. Ask: **What related addition fact could help you solve the subtraction problem?**

- Have children write a related addition sentence on the card using the two numbers given and a missing addend.

- Have children trade cards and fill in the missing numbers. Remind children that the two missing numbers on each card should be the same.

$$14 - 6 = \underline{\hspace{1cm}}$$
$$6 + \underline{\hspace{1cm}} = 14$$

🔺 RtI Response to Intervention

Reteach Tier 1
🕐 | Kinesthetic
Whole Class / Small Group

Materials 2 sheets of paper, two-color counters

- Ask children to fold a sheet of paper in half and draw a line on the fold to separate the paper into two sections.

- Write $7 + 5 = \underline{\hspace{1cm}}$ on the board. Have children place 7 red counters on the left and 5 yellow counters on the right. Then have children find how many counters there are in all. 12 counters Write the answer on the board.

- Then write the subtraction sentence $12 - 7 = 5$ on the board. Have children cover the red counters with the other sheet of paper to model the subtraction sentence.

- Then have children repeat the activity, this time modeling the related facts $8 + 3 = 11$ and $11 - 8 = 3$.

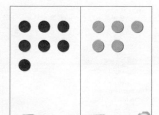

Tier 2
🕐 | Visual
Small Group

- Ask a group of 3 girls and a group of 4 boys to stand in the front of the classroom.

- Have each group count on by ones and tell the number in their group. Write $3 + 4$ on the board.

- Have both groups stand together. Ask: **How many children are there in all?** 7 children Complete the fact on the board: $3 + 4 = 7$.

- To relate this addition fact to subtraction, write 7 on the board. Then ask the group of girls to move to the side. Write $- 3$ next to 7. Ask: **How many children are left?** 4 children Complete the fact on the board: $7 - 3 = 4$.

- Repeat the activity to model the related number sentences $5 + 3 = 8$ and $8 - 5 = 3$.

1 ENGAGE

GO Online **iTools**

Materials *iTools: Counters*

Access Prior Knowledge As you read these problems, use *iTools* counters to model them. Ask children to write a number sentence for each problem.

I have 5 bears, and I find 2 more bears. How many do I have now? 5 + 2 = 7

I have 5 bears, and I lose 2 bears. How many do I have now? 5 − 2 = 3

- **How did you know whether to add or subtract to solve each problem?** Possible answer: I added in the first problem because we put together two groups of bears. I subtracted in the second problem because we took bears away.

2 TEACH and TALK

GO Online **Animated Math Models**

▶ **Listen and Draw** REAL WORLD

Read the first problem. Have children complete the first bar model.

The soccer team has 8 red balls and 7 yellow balls. How many soccer balls does the team have? 15 soccer balls

Direct children's attention to the bracket below the bars. Explain that the bracket shows that the two bars for the parts are being joined to show the whole.

- **How does the bar model at the top of the page help you solve the problem?** Possible answer: The model shows that I need to find the whole.

- **Will you add or subtract to solve for the missing amount?** add

Read the related subtraction problem.

The soccer team has 15 balls inside the locker room. The children took the 7 yellow balls outside. How many soccer balls were inside? 8 soccer balls

- **What information is missing in the bar model for this problem?** the number of soccer balls inside

- **Will you add or subtract to solve for the missing amount?** subtract

Use **Math Talk** to focus on children's understanding of the differences between addition and subtraction.

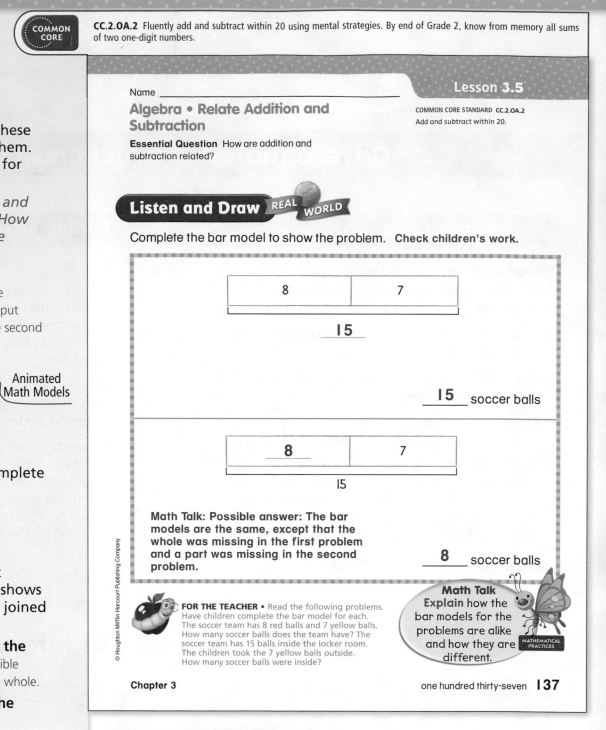

Name _____

Algebra • Relate Addition and Subtraction

Lesson **3.5**

COMMON CORE STANDARD CC.2.OA.2
Add and subtract within 20.

CC.2.OA.2 Fluently add and subtract within 20 using mental strategies. By end of Grade 2, know from memory all sums of two one-digit numbers.

Essential Question How are addition and subtraction related?

Listen and Draw REAL WORLD

Complete the bar model to show the problem. **Check children's work.**

| 8 | 7 |

15

_15_ soccer balls

| 8 | 7 |

15

Math Talk: Possible answer: The bar models are the same, except that the whole was missing in the first problem and a part was missing in the second problem.

_8_ soccer balls

FOR THE TEACHER • Read the following problems. Have children complete the bar model for each. The soccer team has 8 red balls and 7 yellow balls. How many soccer balls does the team have? The soccer team has 15 balls inside the locker room. The children took the 7 yellow balls outside. How many soccer balls were inside?

Math Talk
Explain how the bar models for the problems are alike and how they are different. MATHEMATICAL PRACTICES

Chapter 3

one hundred thirty-seven **137**

Standards Practice 3.5

Common Core

SPIRAL REVIEW

Name _____

Lesson **3.5**

Algebra • Relate Addition and Subtraction

COMMON CORE STANDARD CC.2.OA.2
Add and subtract within 20.

Write the sum and the difference for the related facts.

| 1. 9 + 6 = _15_ | 2. 8 + 5 = _13_ | 3. 9 + 9 = _18_ |
| 15 − 6 = _9_ | 13 − 5 = _8_ | 18 − 9 = _9_ |

| 4. 7 + 3 = _10_ | 5. 7 + 5 = _12_ | 6. 6 + 8 = _14_ |
| 10 − 3 = _7_ | 12 − 5 = _7_ | 14 − 6 = _8_ |

| 7. 6 + 7 = _13_ | 8. 8 + 8 = _16_ | 9. 6 + 4 = _10_ |
| 13 − 6 = _7_ | 16 − 8 = _8_ | 10 − 4 = _6_ |

| 10. 7 + 9 = _16_ | 11. 9 + 4 = _13_ | 12. 8 + 7 = _15_ |
| 16 − 9 = _7_ | 13 − 9 = _4_ | 15 − 7 = _8_ |

PROBLEM SOLVING REAL WORLD

Solve. Write or draw to explain.

13. There are 13 children on the bus. Then 5 children get off the bus. How many children are on the bus now?

_8_ children

Chapter 3

sixty-one **P61**

Lesson Check (CC.2.OA.2)

1. Which is a related addition fact for 15 − 6 = 9?
- ● 9 + 6 = 15
- ○ 3 + 3 = 6
- ○ 6 + 6 = 12
- ○ 3 + 6 = 9

2. Which is a related subtraction fact for 5 + 7 = 12?
- ○ 5 − 2 = 3
- ○ 15 − 5 = 10
- ○ 7 − 5 = 2
- ● 12 − 7 = 5

Spiral Review (CC.2.NBT.1, CC.2.NBT.3, CC.2.NBT.8)

3. Which is another way to write 4 hundreds? (Lesson 2.3)
- ○ 4
- ○ 40
- ● 400
- ○ 440

4. What is the next number in the pattern? (Lesson 2.10)
515, 615, 715, 815, ▢
- ○ 820
- ○ 905
- ● 915
- ○ 920

5. What number is 10 more than 237? (Lesson 2.9)
- ○ 227
- ● 247
- ○ 337
- ○ 347

6. Which is another way to write the number 110? (Lesson 2.7)
- ○ 100 + 10 + 1
- ○ 1 hundred 1 ten 1 one
- ○ one hundred eleven
- ● 100 + 10

★ TEST PREP

P62 sixty-two

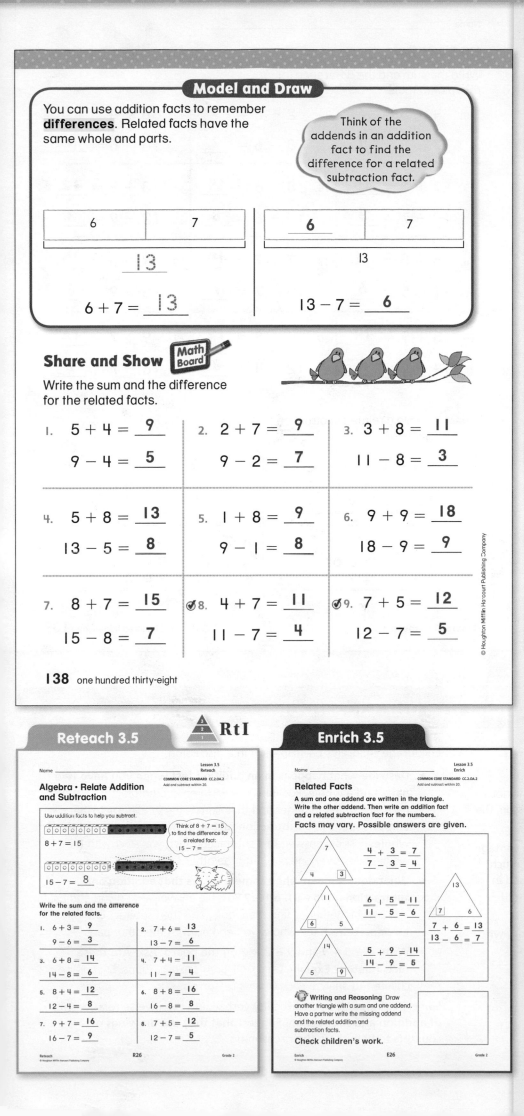

Model and Draw

You can use addition facts to remember **differences**. Related facts have the same whole and parts.

> Think of the addends in an addition fact to find the difference for a related subtraction fact.

6	7

13

$6 + 7 = \underline{13}$

6	7

13

$13 - 7 = \underline{6}$

Share and Show

Math Board

Write the sum and the difference for the related facts.

1. $5 + 4 = \underline{9}$
   $9 - 4 = \underline{5}$

2. $2 + 7 = \underline{9}$
   $9 - 2 = \underline{7}$

3. $3 + 8 = \underline{11}$
   $11 - 8 = \underline{3}$

4. $5 + 8 = \underline{13}$
   $13 - 5 = \underline{8}$

5. $1 + 8 = \underline{9}$
   $9 - 1 = \underline{8}$

6. $9 + 9 = \underline{18}$
   $18 - 9 = \underline{9}$

7. $8 + 7 = \underline{15}$
   $15 - 8 = \underline{7}$

✓8. $4 + 7 = \underline{11}$
   $11 - 7 = \underline{4}$

✓9. $7 + 5 = \underline{12}$
   $12 - 7 = \underline{5}$

138 one hundred thirty-eight

© Houghton Mifflin Harcourt Publishing Company

Reteach 3.5

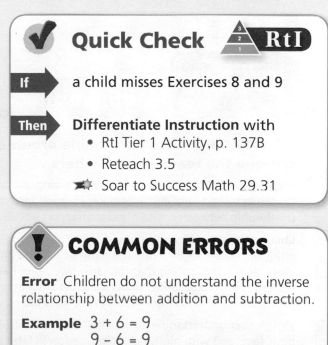

Name ____

Lesson 3.5
Reteach

Algebra • Relate Addition and Subtraction

COMMON CORE STANDARD CC.2.OA.2
Add and subtract within 20.

Use addition facts to help you subtract.

Think of $8 + 7 = 15$ to find the difference for a related fact:
$15 - 7 = \underline{}$

$8 + 7 = 15$

$15 - 7 = \underline{8}$

Write the sum and the difference for the related facts.

1. $6 + 3 = \underline{9}$
   $9 - 6 = \underline{3}$

2. $7 + 6 = \underline{13}$
   $13 - 7 = \underline{6}$

3. $6 + 8 = \underline{14}$
   $14 - 8 = \underline{6}$

4. $7 + 4 = \underline{11}$
   $11 - 7 = \underline{4}$

5. $8 + 4 = \underline{12}$
   $12 - 4 = \underline{8}$

6. $8 + 8 = \underline{16}$
   $16 - 8 = \underline{8}$

7. $9 + 7 = \underline{16}$
   $16 - 7 = \underline{9}$

8. $7 + 5 = \underline{12}$
   $12 - 7 = \underline{5}$

Reteach
© Houghton Mifflin Harcourt Publishing Company

R26

Grade 2

Enrich 3.5

Name ____

Lesson 3.5
Enrich

Related Facts

COMMON CORE STANDARD CC.2.OA.2
Add and subtract within 20.

A sum and one addend are written in the triangle. Write the other addend. Then write an addition fact and a related subtraction fact for the numbers.

Facts may vary. Possible answers are given.

7 / 4 / 3
$4 + 3 = 7$
$7 - 3 = 4$

11 / 6 / 5
$6 + 5 = 11$
$11 - 5 = 6$

14 / 5 / 9
$5 + 9 = 14$
$14 - 9 = 5$

13 / 7 / 6
$7 + 6 = 13$
$13 - 6 = 7$

Writing and Reasoning Draw another triangle with a sum and one addend. Have a partner write the missing addend and the related addition and subtraction facts.

Check children's work.

Enrich
© Houghton Mifflin Harcourt Publishing Company

E26

Grade 2

▶ **Model and Draw**   MATHEMATICAL PRACTICES

Use the bar models to discuss the whole and the parts in the related facts.

- **How are the addition fact and the subtraction fact alike?** They have the same whole, 13, and the same parts, 6 and 7.

- **How can knowing 6 + 7 = 13 help you find the difference for 13 − 7?** Possible answer: I can think about how the facts are related. They have the same whole and one part is the same, so the other part must also be the same. $13 - 7 = 6$

- **Why are the answers for the two problems written in different places on the bar models?** Possible answer: The first problem is an addition problem and we are finding the whole; the second problem is a subtraction problem and we are finding a part.

③ PRACTICE Math Board

▶ **Share and Show** • **Guided Practice**

Exercises 1–9 connect to the learning model.

- **In Exercise 1, how are the two number sentences related?** Possible answer: They have the same whole and the same parts. I know that $5 + 4 = 9$, so $9 - 4 = 5$.

Use Exercises 8 and 9 for **Quick Check**. Children should use their MathBoards to show their solutions to these exercises.

✔ **Quick Check**  RtI

If ▶ a child misses Exercises 8 and 9

Then ▶ **Differentiate Instruction** with
- RtI Tier 1 Activity, p. 137B
- Reteach 3.5
- Soar to Success Math 29.31

⚠ COMMON ERRORS

Error Children do not understand the inverse relationship between addition and subtraction.

Example $3 + 6 = 9$
$9 - 6 = 9$

Springboard to Learning Have children use connecting cubes to model the addition fact and then break apart the train to model and solve the subtraction fact.

▶ On Your Own • Independent Practice

If children answer Exercises 8 and 9 correctly, assign Exercises 10–25.

H.O.T. Problems In Exercises 22–25 children use higher order thinking skills to write a related subtraction fact for an addition fact.

- **How do you use the addition fact to help you write a related subtraction fact?** Possible answer: The addition fact shows the two parts added together to make the whole. For a subtraction fact, I write the whole with one part subtracted from it and the other part as the difference.

You may wish to ask children to write both subtraction facts related to each addition fact.

Go Deeper   MATHEMATICAL PRACTICES

Challenge children to make mathematical connections by writing a story problem for the related facts in one of the H.O.T. problems. Have children draw bar models to show the related facts.

Name _____

On Your Own

Write the sum and the difference for the related facts.

10. $4 + 3 = \underline{7}$
    $7 - 3 = \underline{4}$

11. $2 + 6 = \underline{8}$
    $8 - 6 = \underline{2}$

12. $6 + 4 = \underline{10}$
    $10 - 6 = \underline{4}$

13. $7 + 3 = \underline{10}$
    $10 - 7 = \underline{3}$

14. $8 + 6 = \underline{14}$
    $14 - 6 = \underline{8}$

15. $3 + 9 = \underline{12}$
    $12 - 9 = \underline{3}$

16. $6 + 5 = \underline{11}$
    $11 - 5 = \underline{6}$

17. $7 + 7 = \underline{14}$
    $14 - 7 = \underline{7}$

18. $9 + 6 = \underline{15}$
    $15 - 9 = \underline{6}$

19. $5 + 9 = \underline{14}$
    $14 - 9 = \underline{5}$

20. $4 + 8 = \underline{12}$
    $12 - 4 = \underline{8}$

21. $9 + 7 = \underline{16}$
    $16 - 7 = \underline{9}$

H.O.T. Write a related subtraction fact for each addition fact.

22. $7 + 8 = 15$
    $15 - 8 = 7$ or
    $15 - 7 = 8$

23. $5 + 7 = 12$
    $12 - 7 = 5$ or
    $12 - 5 = 7$

24. $6 + 7 = 13$
    $13 - 7 = 6$ or
    $13 - 6 = 7$

25. $9 + 8 = 17$
    $17 - 8 = 9$ or
    $17 - 9 = 8$

Chapter 3 • Lesson 5   one hundred thirty-nine **139**

Mathematical Practices in Your Classroom

CC.K–12.MP.3 Construct viable arguments and critique the reasoning of others.

Throughout this chapter, children are reviewing and applying various strategies to find sums and differences for basic facts. In this lesson, the relationship between addition and subtraction is reviewed.

Children must understand this inverse relationship from the vantage point of related facts having the same whole and parts. It is much more than just knowing that the same three numbers are used in related facts; it is a deeper understanding of what addition and subtraction are, and *why* certain sets of facts are related.

This deeper understanding can help increase children's fluency with basic facts and with multidigit computation in later chapters.

Encourage children's participation in a discussion.

- **Describe what happens in an addition fact when you have two parts and a whole.** Possible answer: In an addition fact, the two parts are added together and their sum is the whole. **Describe what happens in a subtraction fact with the two parts and the whole.** Possible answer: In a subtraction fact, you start with the whole, take away one part, and the other part is left.

- **What does it mean when someone says that addition and subtraction undo each other?** Possible answer: When you add two parts together to find the whole, and then subtract one of those parts from the whole, you end up with the other part.

- Write $4 + 5 = 9$ and $9 - 2 = 7$ on the board. Ask: **Are these facts related? Explain.** Check children's explanations. Encourage children to analyze each other's reasoning.

Some children may have difficulty verbalizing the inverse relationship of addition and subtraction. Suggest that they use drawings or counters to help show their reasoning.

PROBLEM SOLVING REAL WORLD

Write Math

Solve. Write or draw to explain.

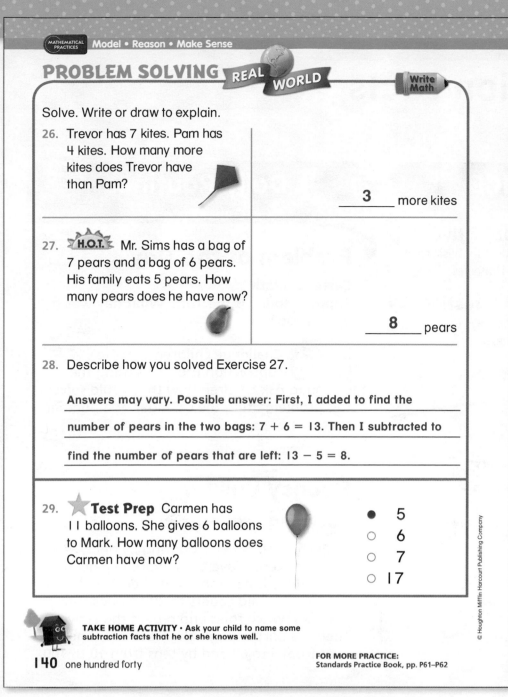

26. Trevor has 7 kites. Pam has 4 kites. How many more kites does Trevor have than Pam?

_____3_____ more kites

27. **H.O.T.** Mr. Sims has a bag of 7 pears and a bag of 6 pears. His family eats 5 pears. How many pears does he have now?

_____8_____ pears

28. Describe how you solved Exercise 27.

Answers may vary. Possible answer: First, I added to find the

number of pears in the two bags: 7 + 6 = 13. Then I subtracted to

find the number of pears that are left: 13 − 5 = 8.

29. ⭐ **Test Prep** Carmen has 11 balloons. She gives 6 balloons to Mark. How many balloons does Carmen have now?

- ● 5
- ○ 6
- ○ 7
- ○ 17

TAKE HOME ACTIVITY · Ask your child to name some subtraction facts that he or she knows well.

FOR MORE PRACTICE:
Standards Practice Book, pp. P61–P62

▶ **Problem Solving** MATHEMATICAL PRACTICES

Have children read Exercise 26. Ask them to describe how they will solve the problem.

Unlock the Problem A key to solving Exercise 26 is recognizing that it is a comparison problem that can be solved by subtracting.

H.O.T. Problem For Exercise 27, children use higher order thinking skills as they solve a multistep problem.

⭐ Test Prep Coach

Test Prep Coach helps teachers to identify common errors that children can make.

In Exercise 29, if children selected:
- **6,** they subtracted incorrectly.
- **7,** they subtracted incorrectly.
- **17,** they added the numbers in the problem.

4 SUMMARIZE MATHEMATICAL PRACTICES

Essential Question

How are addition and subtraction related?
Possible answer: Addition and subtraction undo each other; related addition and subraction facts have the same whole and parts.

Math Journal

Write a related subtraction fact for 3 + 9 = 12. Explain how the two facts are related.

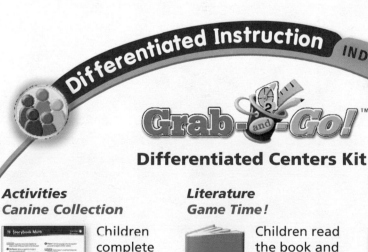

Differentiated Instruction   INDEPENDENT ACTIVITIES

Grab-and-Go!
Differentiated Centers Kit

Activities
Canine Collection

Children complete purple Activity Card 3 by writing related facts using various sets of numbers.

Literature
Game Time!

Children read the book and add or subtract to find shin guards for the soccer players.

Games
Caterpillar Chase

Children practice basic addition facts to move along the game path.

Digital Path

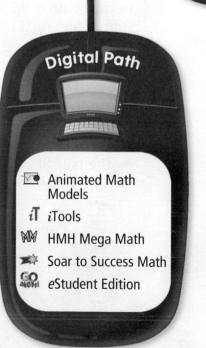

- 📺 Animated Math Models
- 𝑖T iTools
- MM HMH Mega Math
- ⭐ Soar to Success Math
- GO Math! eStudent Edition

Practice Subtraction Facts

LESSON AT A GLANCE

Common Core Standard
Add and subtract within 20.
CC.2.OA.2 Fluently add and subtract within 20 using mental strategies. By end of Grade 2, know from memory all sums of two one-digit numbers.

Lesson Objective
Recall differences for basic facts using mental strategies.

Essential Question
What are some ways to remember differences?

Materials MathBoard

Digital Path

- ☑ Animated Math Models
- 𝕄𝕄 HMH Mega Math
- *i*T *i*Tools: Counters
- 🔵 *e*Student Edition

COMMON CORE
PROFESSIONAL DEVELOPMENT

About the Math

If Children Ask

Children may question why thinking about addition facts can be a good strategy to use to solve subtraction facts.

Review with children how related addition and subtraction facts have the same whole and the same parts.

For the basic fact 6 + 9 = 15, the parts are the addends, 6 and 9; the whole is the sum, 15. Thinking about the addends (or the parts) in this addition fact can help children find the difference (one of the parts) for the related subtraction fact, 15 − 9 = _____.

This addition/subtraction connection is a powerful mathematical tool and can be a very useful strategy for recalling basic facts.

PODCASTING
Professional Development Video Podcasts

Daily Routines
Math Board
Common Core

SPIRAL REVIEW

Problem of the Day

*e*Transparency
3.6

Calendar Math
Suppose today is the 10th. What day was it 4 days ago?

CALENDAR Challenge children to solve subtraction problems using the calendar. Ask children how they could solve this problem using the calendar or a number sentence.

Fluency Builder
Counting Patterns

Have children review counting by ones, fives, and tens. Have them work in pairs. The first child says a number between 1 and 10. The second child counts to 20 by ones. The partners switch roles and repeat the activity. Then the partners will alternate counting by fives from 5 to 60 and by tens from 10 to 100.

Differentiated Instruction Activities

ELL Language Support
🕐 Visual
Small Group

Strategy: Define

- Children can define the word *difference* by using it in context and by matching visuals to the word.

- Show children a subtraction problem with a missing difference. Then show them a set of facts in which only one fact helps find the difference of the subtraction fact. Have children point to the fact that helps them find the difference.

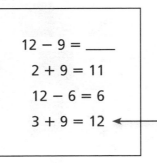

$$12 - 9 = \underline{\hspace{1cm}}$$
$$2 + 9 = 11$$
$$12 - 6 = 6$$
$$3 + 9 = 12 \longleftarrow$$

- Use the word *difference* to describe the answer to a subtraction problem.

See **ELL** Activity Guide for leveled activities.

Enrich
🕐 Visual
Partners

Materials 2 sets of Secret Code Cards 1–10, *Count On Me* Game Board (see *eTeacher Resources*), color paper

- Players fold their game board and use the subtraction side. Set 1 of the cards is placed above the game board. Player 2 holds the other set.

- Player 1 chooses a total from the set of cards above the game board and places the card or cards in the first blank space. Be sure the total is greater than 2.

- Player 2 selects two cards from Set 2 that have a sum equal to the total and places them in the remaining two boxes. Player 2 covers the difference with a piece of color paper.

- Player 1 says the correct unknown number. When Player 1 gets the correct answer, players switch roles, and the game continues.

RtI Response to Intervention

Reteach Tier 1
🕐 Visual / Kinesthetic
Whole Class / Small Group

Materials two-color counters

- Write $9 - 3 = \underline{\hspace{1cm}}$ on the board. Ask: **How can you use counters to model this fact?** Possible answer: Count out 9 red counters and take away 3 counters.

- Model using the counters to find the difference by counting back. Start with 9 counters. Say "9" as you point to the ninth counter. As you take away one counter at a time, count back aloud 8, 7, 6. **So, 9 − 3 = 6.**

- Now model for children how to think of a subtraction fact as an addition fact with a missing addend. Write $3 + \underline{\hspace{1cm}} = 9$ on the board. With the 9 counters organized as a group of 3 and a group of 6, have children identify the missing addend. 6

- **So, to find the difference for 9 − 3, we can think 3 plus what number is 9? The missing number in the addition fact is the difference between 9 and 3.**

Tier 2
🕐 Visual / Kinesthetic
Small Group

Materials two-color counters

- Remind children that in subtraction you take away a part from the whole to find the other part and that in addition you put parts together to make a whole.

- Write $6 - 2$ on the board. Ask: **What is the whole?** 6 Model 6 with counters. Then ask: **How many counters are you taking away?** 2 counters Point to the sixth counter and say "6." Take away one counter at a time and count back aloud 5, 4. **How many counters are left?** 4 counters

- Then explain that the same subtraction problem can be solved in a different way. **The parts that make a whole in an addition fact can be used to find the missing part in a subtraction problem.**

- Model 6 as a group of 2 counters and a group of 4 counters. **These counters show that 2 + 4 = 6. So, the difference between 6 and 2 is 4.**

1 ENGAGE

Access Prior Knowledge Review related addition and subtraction facts. Write *5 + 3 = 8* on the board. Then have children name a related subtraction fact. 8 − 3 = 5 or 8 − 5 = 3

- **How does the subtraction fact undo the addition fact?** Possible answer: When I add, I start with 5, add 3, and get the sum 8. When I subtract, I start with 8, take away 3, and get 5, which is the number I started with.

2 TEACH and TALK

 Animated Math Models

▶ **Listen and Draw**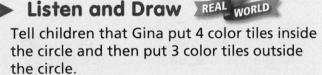

Tell children that Gina put 4 color tiles inside the circle and then put 3 color tiles outside the circle.

- **What addition fact could be written for Gina's model?** Possible answers: 4 + 3 = 7, or 3 + 4 = 7

- **How does this addition fact show Gina's model?** Possible answer: The addition fact shows the two parts added together to make the whole. The number of tiles inside the circle and the number of tiles outside the circle are the parts. The total number of tiles is the whole.

Now have children look again at the picture of Gina's model. Tell them that Gina put 3 color tiles outside the circle and then put 4 color tiles inside the circle.

- **What addition fact could be written for Gina's model?** Possible answers: 4 + 3 = 7, or 3 + 4 = 7

Now have children look again at the picture of Gina's model. Tell them that there were 7 tiles outside the circle. Then Gina moved 4 of the tiles to be inside the circle.

- **What subtraction fact could be written for Gina's model?** 7 − 4 = 3

Now have children look again at the picture of Gina's model. Tell them that there were 7 tiles inside the circle. Then Gina moved 3 of the tiles to be outside the circle.

- **What subtraction fact could be written for Gina's model?** 7 − 3 = 4

Use **Math Talk** to focus on children's understanding of how addition and subtraction facts are related.

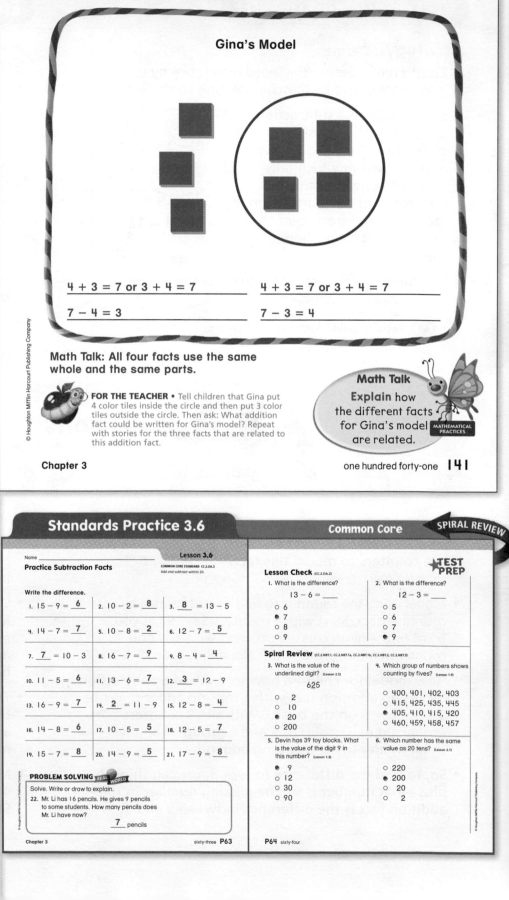

CC.2.OA.2 Fluently add and subtract within 20 using mental strategies. By end of Grade 2, know from memory all sums of two one-digit numbers.

Name _____

Lesson 3.6

Practice Subtraction Facts

COMMON CORE STANDARD CC.2.OA.2
Add and subtract within 20.

Essential Question What are some ways to remember differences?

Listen and Draw REAL WORLD

Use Gina's model to answer the question.

Gina's Model

| 4 + 3 = 7 or 3 + 4 = 7 | 4 + 3 = 7 or 3 + 4 = 7 |
| 7 − 4 = 3 | 7 − 3 = 4 |

Math Talk: All four facts use the same whole and the same parts.

FOR THE TEACHER • Tell children that Gina put 4 color tiles inside the circle and then put 3 color tiles outside the circle. Then ask: What addition fact could be written for Gina's model? Repeat with stories for the three facts that are related to this addition fact.

Math Talk
Explain how the different facts for Gina's model are related.
MATHEMATICAL PRACTICES

Chapter 3

one hundred forty-one **141**

Standards Practice 3.6

Common Core • SPIRAL REVIEW

Name _____

Lesson 3.6

Practice Subtraction Facts

COMMON CORE STANDARD CC.2.OA.2
Add and subtract within 20.

Write the difference.

1. 15 − 9 = _6_
2. 10 − 2 = _8_
3. _8_ = 13 − 5
4. 14 − 7 = _7_
5. 10 − 8 = _2_
6. 12 − 7 = _5_
7. _7_ = 10 − 3
8. 16 − 7 = _9_
9. 8 − 4 = _4_
10. 11 − 5 = _6_
11. 13 − 6 = _7_
12. _3_ = 12 − 9
13. 16 − 9 = _7_
14. _2_ = 11 − 9
15. 12 − 8 = _4_
16. 14 − 8 = _6_
17. 10 − 5 = _5_
18. 12 − 5 = _7_
19. 15 − 7 = _8_
20. 14 − 9 = _5_
21. 17 − 9 = _8_

PROBLEM SOLVING REAL WORLD

Solve. Write or draw to explain.

22. Mr. Li has 16 pencils. He gives 9 pencils to some students. How many pencils does Mr. Li have now?

_7_ pencils

Chapter 3

sixty-three **P63**

Lesson Check (CC.2.OA.2)

★TEST PREP

1. What is the difference?

13 − 6 = ___

- ○ 6
- ● 7
- ○ 8
- ○ 9

2. What is the difference?

12 − 3 = ___

- ○ 5
- ○ 6
- ○ 7
- ● 9

Spiral Review (CC.2.NBT.1, CC.2.NBT.1a, CC.2.NBT.1b, CC.2.NBT.2, CC.2.NBT.3)

3. What is the value of the underlined digit? (Lesson 2.1)

6**2**5

- ○ 2
- ○ 10
- ● 20
- ○ 200

4. Which group of numbers shows counting by fives? (Lesson 1.8)

- ○ 400, 401, 402, 403
- ○ 415, 425, 435, 445
- ● 405, 410, 415, 420
- ○ 460, 459, 458, 457

5. Devin has 39 toy blocks. What is the value of the digit 9 in this number? (Lesson 1.3)

- ● 9
- ○ 12
- ○ 30
- ○ 90

6. Which number has the same value as 20 tens? (Lesson 2.1)

- ○ 220
- ● 200
- ○ 20
- ○ 2

P64 sixty-four

Model and Draw

These are some ways to find differences.

You can count back by 1, 2, or 3.

$7 - 3 = \underline{4}$

Start with 7.
Say: 6, 5, 4.

$9 - 3 = \underline{6}$

Start with 9.
Say: 8, 7, 6.

You can think about a missing addend to subtract.

$8 - 5 = \blacksquare$

$5 + 3 = 8$

So, $8 - 5 = \underline{3}$.

Share and Show

Write the difference.

1. $6 - 4 = \underline{2}$
2. $10 - 7 = \underline{3}$
3. $\underline{3} = 5 - 2$
4. $14 - 6 = \underline{8}$
5. $8 - 4 = \underline{4}$
6. $11 - 3 = \underline{8}$
7. $\underline{2} = 7 - 5$
8. $6 - 5 = \underline{1}$
9. $5 - 0 = \underline{5}$
10. $13 - 9 = \underline{4}$
11. $9 - 3 = \underline{6}$
12. $\underline{1} = 7 - 6$
13. $12 - 3 = \underline{9}$
14. $6 - 3 = \underline{3}$
15. $9 - 5 = \underline{4}$
16. $10 - 4 = \underline{6}$
17. $\underline{5} = 8 - 3$
18. $13 - 5 = \underline{8}$

© Houghton Mifflin Harcourt Publishing Company

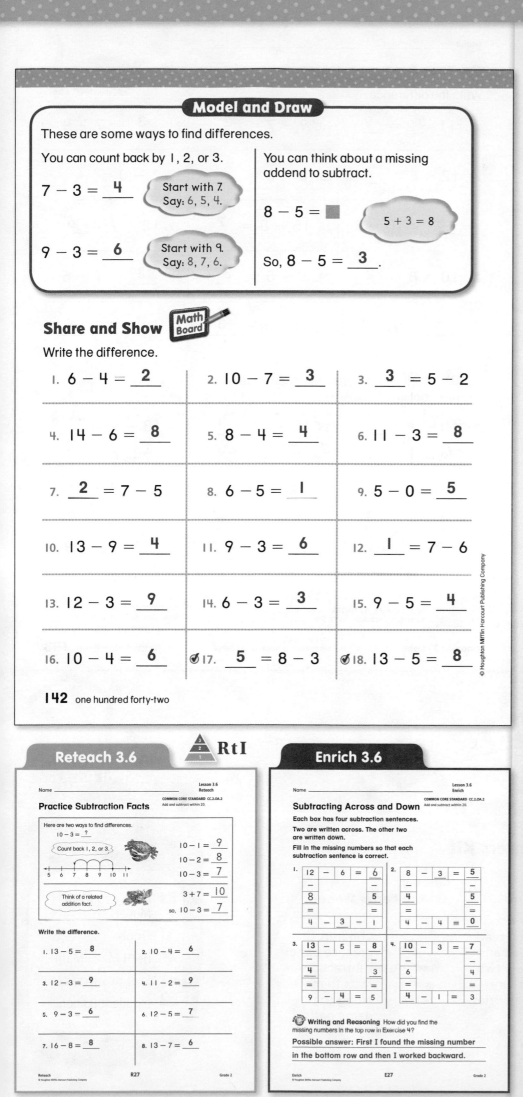

▶ On Your Own • Independent Practice

If children answer Exercises 17 and 18 correctly, assign Exercises 19–36.

H.O.T. Problems In Exercises 34–36, children solve four facts, look for a pattern in the facts, and then write the next fact in the pattern.

- **Describe the pattern in the facts in Exercise 34.** Possible answer: The first number in each fact is 2 less than the first number in the fact before it. 1 is being subtracted in each fact. Each difference is 2 less than the difference in the fact before it.

Go Deeper
MATHEMATICAL PRACTICES

Give children the subtraction expressions below. Ask them to identify a strategy that they can use to find each difference.

11 − 9	8 − 3	5 − 4	10 − 7
6 − 5	8 − 2	10 − 5	9 − 6

4 SUMMARIZE
MATHEMATICAL PRACTICES

Essential Question

What are some ways to remember differences? Possible answer: I could use a related addition fact or count back by 1, 2, or 3.

Math Journal

Write or draw to explain two different ways to find the difference for 12 − 3.

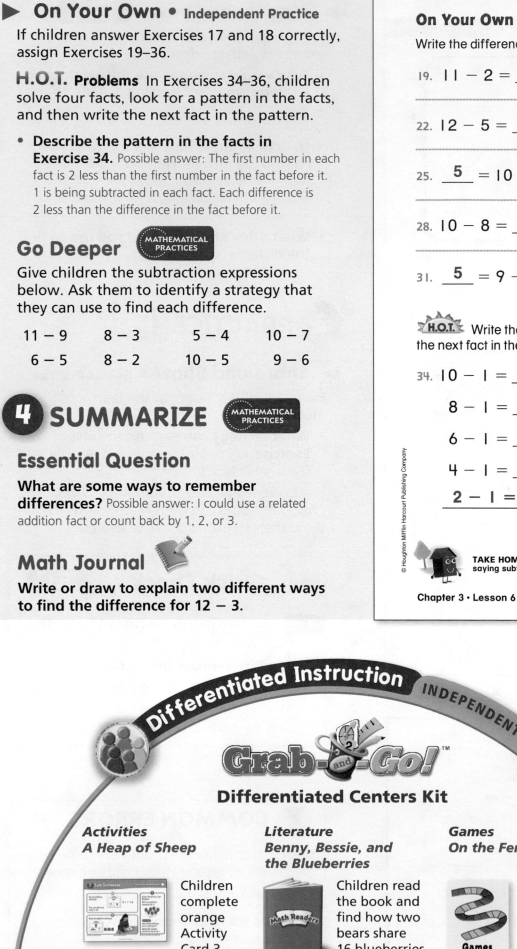

Name _____

On Your Own

Write the difference.

19. $11 - 2 = \underline{9}$ 20. $9 - 7 = \underline{2}$ 21. $\underline{3} = 7 - 4$

22. $12 - 5 = \underline{7}$ 23. $8 - 6 = \underline{2}$ 24. $7 - 0 = \underline{7}$

25. $\underline{5} = 10 - 5$ 26. $15 - 8 = \underline{7}$ 27. $13 - 7 = \underline{6}$

28. $10 - 8 = \underline{2}$ 29. $8 - 5 = \underline{3}$ 30. $\underline{3} = 9 - 6$

31. $\underline{5} = 9 - 4$ 32. $11 - 8 = \underline{3}$ 33. $12 - 7 = \underline{5}$

H.O.T. Write the differences. Then write the next fact in the pattern.

34. $10 - 1 = \underline{9}$
$8 - 1 = \underline{7}$
$6 - 1 = \underline{5}$
$4 - 1 = \underline{3}$
$2 - 1 = 1$

35. $12 - 9 = \underline{3}$
$13 - 9 = \underline{4}$
$14 - 9 = \underline{5}$
$15 - 9 = \underline{6}$
$16 - 9 = 7$

36. $18 - 9 = \underline{9}$
$17 - 8 = \underline{9}$
$16 - 7 = \underline{9}$
$15 - 6 = \underline{9}$
$14 - 5 = 9$

TAKE HOME ACTIVITY · With your child, practice saying subtraction facts from this lesson.

FOR EXTRA PRACTICE: Standards Practice Book, p. P75

Chapter 3 · Lesson 6   **FOR MORE PRACTICE:** Standards Practice Book, pp. P63–P64   one hundred forty-three **143**

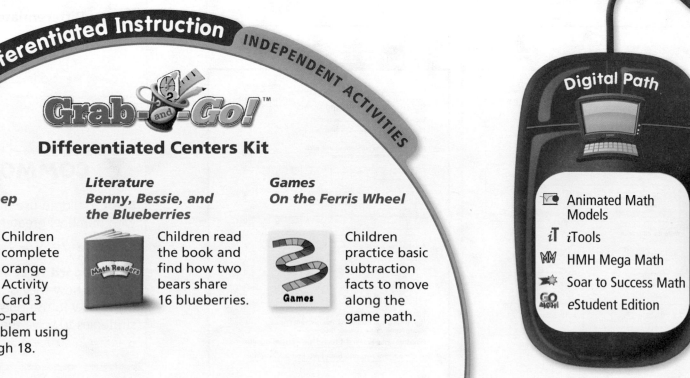

Differentiated Instruction
INDEPENDENT ACTIVITIES

Grab-and-Go!™
Differentiated Centers Kit

Activities
A Heap of Sheep

Children complete orange Activity Card 3 by solving a two-part subtraction problem using numbers through 18.

Literature
Benny, Bessie, and the Blueberries

Children read the book and find how two bears share 16 blueberries.

Games
On the Ferris Wheel

Children practice basic subtraction facts to move along the game path.

Digital Path

- ▣ Animated Math Models
- iT iTools
- MM HMH Mega Math
- ★ Soar to Success Math
- GO eStudent Edition

Name _____

✓ Mid-Chapter Checkpoint

Concepts and Skills

Write the sum. (CC.2.OA.2)

1. $3 + 6 = \underline{9}$	2. $8 + 0 = \underline{8}$	3. $7 + 7 = \underline{14}$
4. $9 + 4 = \underline{13}$	5. $\underline{11} = 5 + 6$	6. $2 + 8 = \underline{10}$
7. $3 + 7 + 2 = \underline{12}$	8. $4 + 4 + 6 = \underline{14}$	

Show how you can make a ten to find the sum.
Write the sum. (CC.2.OA.2)

9. $9 + 7 = \underline{16}$

$10 + \underline{6} = \underline{16}$

10. $6 + 8 = \underline{14}$

$10 + \underline{4} = \underline{14}$

Write the sum and the difference for the related facts. (CC.2.OA.2)

11. $5 + 4 = \underline{9}$	12. $3 + 9 = \underline{12}$	13. $8 + 7 = \underline{15}$
$9 - 4 = \underline{5}$	$12 - 9 = \underline{3}$	$15 - 8 = \underline{7}$

⭐ Test Prep (CC.2.OA.2)

14. There are 9 flute players and 4 trumpet players in the band. How many flute players and trumpet players are there?

- ○ 14
- ● 13
- ○ 11
- ○ 5

144 one hundred forty-four

© Houghton Mifflin Harcourt Publishing Company

✓ Data-Driven Decision Making ▲RtI

Based on the results of the Mid-Chapter Checkpoint, use the following resources to strengthen individual or whole class instruction.

Item	Lesson	*CCSS	Common Error	Intervene With	Soar to Success Math
1–6	3.1, 3.2	CC.2.OA.2	May not use the addition strategies or properties correctly	R—3.1, 3.2; TE—pp. 121B, 125B	10.19, 10.23
7, 8	3.4	CC.2.OA.2	May not add the third addend to find the total sum	R—3.4; TE—p. 133B	10.24
9, 10	3.3	CC.2.OA.2	May incorrectly break the addend into a combination that does not make a ten	R—3.3; TE—p. 129B	10.20
11–13	3.5	CC.2.OA.2	May not realize that the two problems are related facts and have the same whole and parts	R—3.5; TE—p. 137B	29.31
14	3.6	CC.2.OA.2	May subtract rather than add	R—3.6; TE—p. 141B	11.15

*CCSS—Common Core State Standard   Key: R—Reteach Book; TE—RtI Activities

Formative Assessment

Use the **Mid-Chapter Checkpoint** to assess children's learning and progress in the first half of the chapter. The formative assessment provides the opportunity to adjust teaching methods for individual or whole class instruction.

Use Ten to Subtract

LESSON AT A GLANCE

Common Core Standard
Add and subtract within 20.
CC.2.OA.2 Fluently add and subtract within 20 using mental strategies. By end of Grade 2, know from memory all sums of two one-digit numbers.

Also CC.2.MD.6

Lesson Objective
Find differences on a number line to develop the mental strategy of decomposing to simplify facts.

Essential Question
How does getting to 10 in subtraction help when finding differences?

Materials MathBoard

Digital Path

iT *i*Tools: Number Lines

GO MATH! eStudent Edition

COMMON CORE PROFESSIONAL DEVELOPMENT

About the Math

Why Teach This?

By encouraging children to work flexibly with numbers, both their number sense and their computation skills can be strengthened.

In this lesson, children use the benchmark number 10 when finding differences for basic facts. Number lines are included in the lesson as a visual aid to reinforce this mental math strategy. This is just one of several strategies that children can use to solve basic subtraction facts. In later chapters, this strategy can be used in multidigit subtraction problems.

 PODCASTING

Professional Development Video Podcasts

Daily Routines

Math Board

Common Core

SPIRAL REVIEW

Problem of the Day

eTransparency 3.7

Basic Facts Complete the subtraction sentences.

$10 - 3 =$ _____ 7
$10 - 5 =$ _____ 5
$10 - 1 =$ _____ 9

Vocabulary Builder

Differences and Sums

Review differences and sums with children by asking them to complete tasks such as the following:

- **Write a number sentence in which the difference is 5.** Possible answer: $8 - 3 = 5$

- **Write a number sentence in which the sum is 8.** Possible answer: $5 + 3 = 8$

Literature

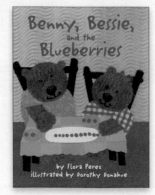

From the Grab-and-Go™ Differentiated Centers Kit

Children read the book and find how two bears share 16 blueberries.

Benny, Bessie, and the Blueberries

Differentiated Instruction Activities

(ELL) Language Support
⏱ Kinesthetic
Small Group

Strategy: Describe

Materials Number Lines (blank) (see *eTeacher Resources*)

- Children practice their comprehension by describing in words and in writing what they have seen.

- Draw two number lines on the board: one that shows 13 – 3 = 10 and one that shows 15 – 5 = 10.

- **Have children describe the pictures.** Possible answer: I see that 3 places to the left of 13 is 10. I see that 5 places to the left of 15 is 10.

- Point out to children that the number lines show subtraction. Ask children to write the number sentence that matches each number line. 13 – 3 = 10; 15 – 5 = 10.

See (ELL) Activity Guide for leveled activities.

Enrich
⏱ Kinesthetic / Interpersonal
Partners

Materials index cards

- Make two sets of index cards with subtraction expressions written on them. Set 1 has expressions with 10 as the minuend. Set 2 has a teen number as the minuend. Each card in Set 1 has the same difference as one card in Set 2.

- Give pairs of children both sets of cards. Have them shuffle all the cards and place them facedown in rows and columns.

- Have children play a matching game in which they turn over two cards at a time and try to find pairs of cards with the same difference.

RtI Response to Intervention

Reteach Tier 1
⏱ Kinesthetic / Visual
Whole Class / Small Group

Materials Number Lines (blank) (see *eTeacher Resources*)

- Write *14 – 6 = ____* on the board. Display a number line labeled from 0 to 20.

- Draw a point at 14. Explain that you will break the 6 apart and subtract in steps. Draw a loop to show a "jump" from 14 to 13 and count 1. Continue until you reach 10 and count 4.

- **What was subtracted from 14 to get to 10?** 4 Circle 14 to 10 on the number line and label the section *4*.

- Draw two more loops from 10 to 8 on the number line and count aloud: 1, 2. **What was subtracted from 10 to get to 8?** 2 Discuss with children that once they got to 10, they used a tens fact to solve. Show children how they subtracted 6 in all on the number line. So, 14 – 6 = 8.

Tier 2
⏱ Kinesthetic / Visual
Small Group

Materials Ten Frames (see *eTeacher Resources*), two-color counters

- On the board, write *15 – 8*. Show 15 counters on ten frames. Move 5 counters off the second ten frame. Leave the pile of 5 counters in view of children.

- **We have subtracted 5 from 15. How many counters are there now?** 10 counters Write *15 – 5 = 10*.

- **We need to subtract 3 more counters to subtract 8 counters in all.** Move 3 counters off the ten frame. Put them with the pile of 5 counters. **How many counters are there now?** 7 counters Write *10 – 3 = 7*.

- Allow children to count the pile of 8 counters to confirm that 8 counters in all were taken away from the 15 counters. Write *15 – 8 = 7*.

- Have children use ten frames and counters to repeat the activity and reinforce their understanding.

1 ENGAGE 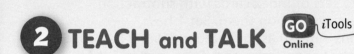 GO Online iTools

Materials iTools: Number Lines

Access Prior Knowledge Introduce the number line to model the subtraction fact 6 − 2 = 4. Demonstrate how to start at the first number, 6, and jump back by the second number, 2. Repeat the activity for 5 − 4 = 1. Be sure children understand that the number you end on is the difference.

2 TEACH and TALK GO Online iTools

▶ Listen and Draw REAL WORLD

Read the following problem aloud.

Scott has 13 crayons. He gives 3 crayons to Tyler. How many crayons does Scott have now?

• **Will you add or subtract to solve?** subtract

Have children circle the part of the blue line segment on the first number line to show what is subtracted from 13.

• **What is the difference?** 10 crayons

Then read the following problem aloud.

Diane has 17 crayons. She gives 7 crayons to Anthony. How many crayons does Diane have now?

Guide a similar discussion about this problem. Have children circle the part of the blue line segment on the second number line to show what is subtracted from 17.

Then read this final problem aloud.

James has 12 crayons. He gives 2 crayons to Cassie. How many crayons does James have now?

Discuss this problem. Have children circle the part of the blue line segment on the third number line to show what is subtracted from 12.

Use Math Talk to focus on children's understanding of what is subtracted from a teens number to get to 10.

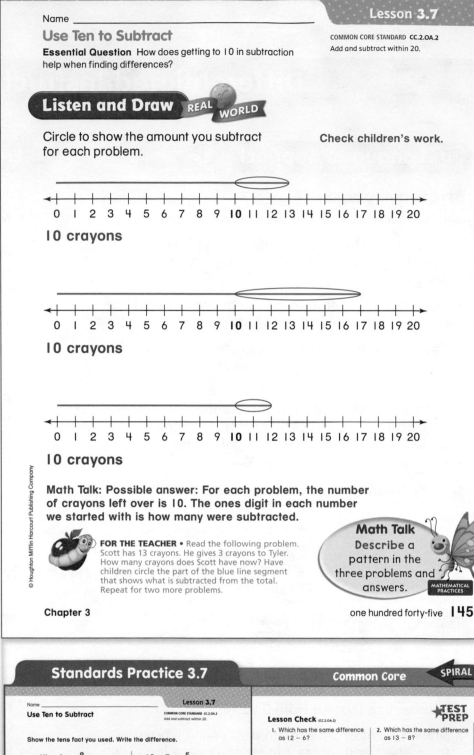

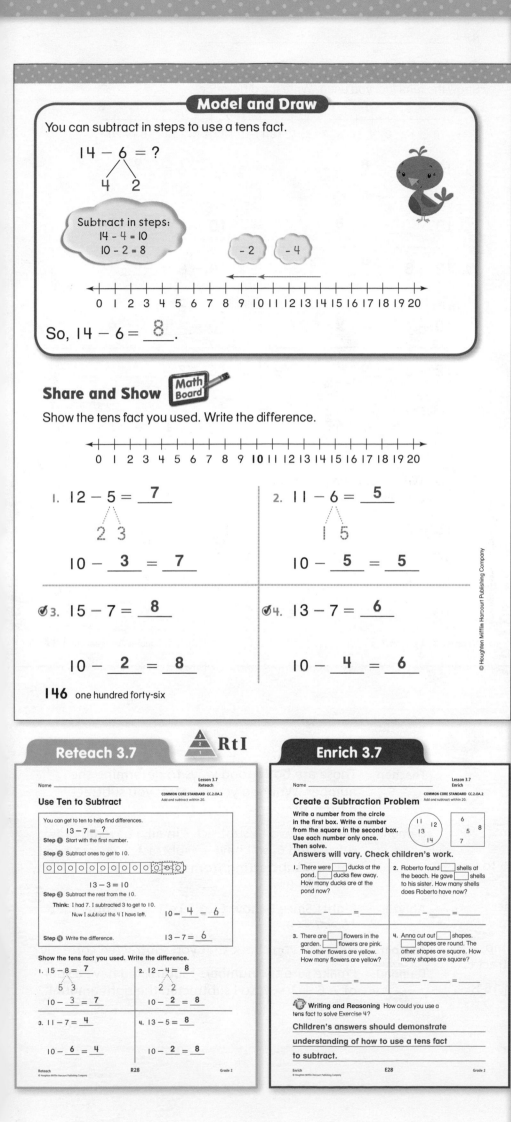

Model and Draw

You can subtract in steps to use a tens fact.

$14 - 6 = ?$

4   2

Subtract in steps:
$14 - 4 = 10$
$10 - 2 = 8$

-2 -4

0 1 2 3 4 5 6 7 8 9 10 11 12 13 14 15 16 17 18 19 20

So, $14 - 6 = \underline{8}$.

Share and Show

Show the tens fact you used. Write the difference.

0 1 2 3 4 5 6 7 8 9 **10** 11 12 13 14 15 16 17 18 19 20

1. $12 - 5 = \underline{7}$

   2 3

   $10 - \underline{3} = 7$

2. $11 - 6 = \underline{5}$

   1 5

   $10 - \underline{5} = 5$

3. $15 - 7 = \underline{8}$

   2 5

   $10 - \underline{2} = 8$

4. $13 - 7 = \underline{6}$

   $10 - \underline{4} = 6$

146 one hundred forty-six

© Houghton Mifflin Harcourt Publishing Company

Reteach 3.7 — RtI

Name _____ Lesson 3.7 Reteach

Use Ten to Subtract COMMON CORE STANDARD CC.2.OA.2 Add and subtract within 20.

You can get to ten to help find differences.

$13 - 7 = ?$

Step 1 Start with the first number.

Step 2 Subtract ones to get to 10.

$13 - 3 = 10$

Step 3 Subtract the rest from the 10.

Think: I had 7. I subtracted 3 to get to 10. Now I subtract the 4 I have left. $10 - \underline{4} = \underline{6}$

Step 4 Write the difference. $13 - 7 = \underline{6}$

Show the tens fact you used. Write the difference.

1. $15 - 8 = \underline{7}$
   5 3
   $10 - \underline{3} = 7$

2. $12 - 4 = \underline{8}$
   2 2
   $10 - \underline{2} = 8$

3. $11 - 7 = \underline{4}$
   $10 - \underline{6} = 4$

4. $13 - 5 = \underline{8}$
   $10 - \underline{2} = 8$

Reteach   R28   Grade 2
© Houghton Mifflin Harcourt Publishing Company

Enrich 3.7

Name _____ Lesson 3.7 Enrich

Create a Subtraction Problem COMMON CORE STANDARD CC.2.OA.2 Add and subtract within 20.

Write a number from the circle in the first box. Write a number from the square in the second box. Use each number only once. Then solve.

11 12
13
14

6
5 8
7

Answers will vary. Check children's work.

1. There were ☐ ducks at the pond. ☐ ducks flew away. How many ducks are at the pond now?

   ___ − ___ = ___

2. Roberto found ☐ shells at the beach. He gave ☐ shells to his sister. How many shells does Roberto have now?

   ___ − ___ = ___

3. There are ☐ flowers in the garden. ☐ flowers are pink. The other flowers are yellow. How many flowers are yellow?

   ___ − ___ = ___

4. Anna cut out ☐ shapes. ☐ shapes are round. The other shapes are square. How many shapes are square?

   ___ − ___ = ___

Writing and Reasoning How could you use a tens fact to solve Exercise 4?

Children's answers should demonstrate understanding of how to use a tens fact to subtract.

Enrich   E28   Grade 2
© Houghton Mifflin Harcourt Publishing Company

Model and Draw

Work through the model with children. Discuss with children what a tens fact is. Point out that by subtracting 4 and then 2, they subtract a total of 6 from 14.

- **Why is 6 broken apart as 4 and 2?**
  Possible answer: To get to 10, we need to subtract 4 from 14. $4 + 2 = 6$, so we need to subtract 2 more.

3 PRACTICE Math Board

Share and Show • Guided Practice

Exercises 1–4 connect to the learning model. Have children first find what they need to subtract to get to 10 and then show the tens fact they used to find the difference.

- **In Exercise 1, how did you find the tens fact to use for the problem?** Possible answer: I subtract 2 from 12 to get to 10. I need to subtract 3 more to subtract 5 in all, so I use the tens fact $10 - 3 = 7$.

Use Exercises 3 and 4 for **Quick Check**. Children should use their MathBoards to show their solutions to these exercises.

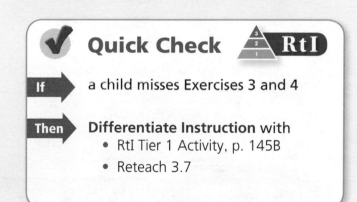

Quick Check RtI

If a child misses Exercises 3 and 4

Then **Differentiate Instruction** with
- RtI Tier 1 Activity, p. 145B
- Reteach 3.7

! COMMON ERRORS

Error Children use the wrong tens fact.

Example In Exercise 3, children write the tens fact $10 - 5 = 5$.

Springboard to Learning Have children look at the marks and the pair of numbers below the subtrahend in Exercise 1. Discuss why the number being subtracted is broken apart in this way. Have children draw marks and write pairs of numbers below the other subtrahends so that they can keep track of their work as they complete the exercises.

147 Chapter 3

▶ **On Your Own** • Independent Practice

If children answer Exercises 3 and 4 correctly, assign Exercises 5–14.

H.O.T. Problem In Exercises 11–14, children use higher order thinking skills to find the missing number that makes two expressions equal. Suggest that children write the difference above the first expression and use that difference to help them find the missing number in the other expression.

Go Deeper MATHEMATICAL PRACTICES

To extend thinking, have children make connections between subtraction facts and tens facts. Give children a tens fact, such as 10 − 3 = 7. Ask children to work in pairs to write two subtraction sentences that they can use this tens fact to help them solve. Possible answers: 15 − 8 = ■, 12 − 5 = ■

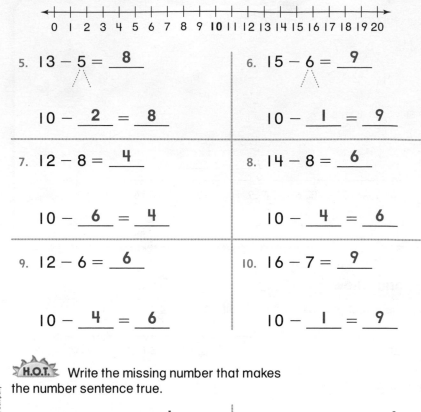

Name _____

On Your Own

Show the tens fact you used. Write the difference.

```
0  1  2  3  4  5  6  7  8  9  10 11 12 13 14 15 16 17 18 19 20
```

5. 13 − 5 = __8__

10 − __2__ = __8__

6. 15 − 6 = __9__

10 − __1__ = __9__

7. 12 − 8 = __4__

10 − __6__ = __4__

8. 14 − 8 = __6__

10 − __4__ = __6__

9. 12 − 6 = __6__

10 − __4__ = __6__

10. 16 − 7 = __9__

10 − __1__ = __9__

H.O.T. Write the missing number that makes the number sentence true.

11. 15 − 6 = 10 − __1__

12. 11 − 7 = 10 − __6__

13. 13 − 6 = 10 − __3__

14. 16 − 8 = 10 − __2__

© Houghton Mifflin Harcourt Publishing Company

Chapter 3 · Lesson 7   one hundred forty-seven **147**

COMMON CORE
PROFESSIONAL DEVELOPMENT   **Math Talk in Action**

The class is discussing Exercise 10.

Teacher: What is the first thing you need to decide when you use a tens fact to help subtract 7 from 16?

Ahlyza: I need to find a number to subtract from 16 to get to 10.

Teacher: How do you decide what number to subtract from 16?

Matthew: I think of a number line. I know I need to jump back 6 to go from 16 to 10, so I need to subtract 6.

Natalie: I use patterns. I know that the ones digit in 16 is 6, so if I subtract 6, I will end up with 10.

Teacher: Those are both good ways to determine the number. What do you do after you subtract 6 from 16?

Damond: I know I have to subtract 7 in all. I have already subtracted 6, so I have to subtract 1 more. Since I am now subtracting from 10, I can use a tens fact, 10 − 1 = 9.

Ahlyza: Right! Since I know that 10 − 1 = 9, I know that 16 − 7 = 9.

Teacher: How can you check that you subtracted correctly?

Damond: I make sure the numbers I subtracted have a sum of 7: 6 + 1 = 7, so I subtracted the right amount.

PROBLEM SOLVING

Write Math

H.O.T. Write number sentences that use both addition and subtraction. Use each choice only once.

Order of answers may vary. Expressions that should be used together are given.

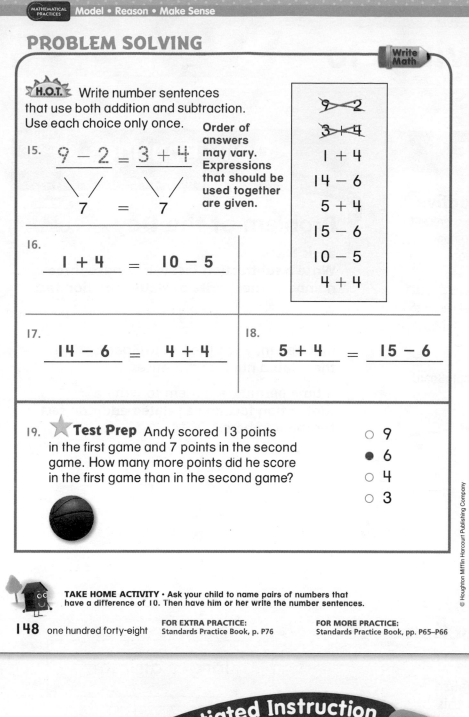

15. $9 - 2 = 3 + 4$

$$7 = 7$$

$$\cancel{9 - 2}$$
$$\cancel{3 + 4}$$
$$1 + 4$$
$$14 - 6$$
$$5 + 4$$
$$15 - 6$$
$$10 - 5$$
$$4 + 4$$

16. $1 + 4 = 10 - 5$

17. $14 - 6 = 4 + 4$

18. $5 + 4 = 15 - 6$

19. ⭐ **Test Prep** Andy scored 13 points in the first game and 7 points in the second game. How many more points did he score in the first game than in the second game?

- ○ 9
- ● 6
- ○ 4
- ○ 3

TAKE HOME ACTIVITY · Ask your child to name pairs of numbers that have a difference of 10. Then have him or her write the number sentences.

FOR EXTRA PRACTICE:
Standards Practice Book, p. P76

FOR MORE PRACTICE:
Standards Practice Book, pp. P65–P66

▶ **Problem Solving** *MATHEMATICAL PRACTICES*

H.O.T. Problems Exercises 15–18 require children to use higher order thinking skills to find both an addition and a subtraction expression with the same value. Guide children through Exercise 15 and then discuss strategies children might use to complete the other three number sentences.

⭐ **Test Prep Coach**

Test Prep Coach helps teachers to identify common errors that children can make.

In Exercise 19, if children selected:

- **9,** they subtracted incorrectly.
- **4,** they chose the number that is subtracted from 10.
- **3,** they chose the number that is subtracted from 13 to get to 10.

4 SUMMARIZE *MATHEMATICAL PRACTICES*

Essential Question

How does getting to 10 in subtraction help when finding differences? Possible answer: If I get to 10, then I can use a tens fact to find the difference.

Math Journal

Describe how to use a tens fact to find the difference for 15 − 8.

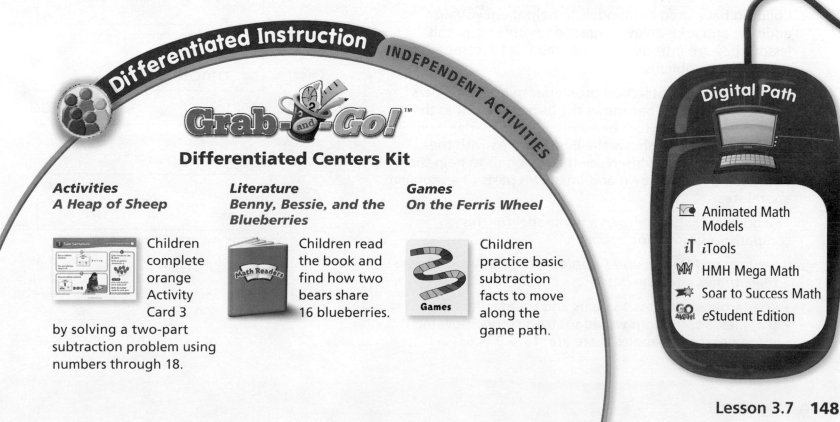

Differentiated Instruction — **INDEPENDENT ACTIVITIES**

Grab-and-Go!™

Differentiated Centers Kit

Activities
A Heap of Sheep

Children complete orange Activity Card 3 by solving a two-part subtraction problem using numbers through 18.

Literature
Benny, Bessie, and the Blueberries

Children read the book and find how two bears share 16 blueberries.

Games
On the Ferris Wheel

Children practice basic subtraction facts to move along the game path.

Digital Path

- 📺 Animated Math Models
- *i*T *i*Tools
- MM HMH Mega Math
- ⭐ Soar to Success Math
- GO MATH *e*Student Edition

Algebra • Use Drawings to Represent Problems

LESSON AT A GLANCE

Common Core Standard
Represent and solve problems involving addition and subtraction.
CC.2.OA.1 Use addition and subtraction within 100 to solve one- and two-step word problems involving situations of adding to, taking from, putting together, taking apart, and comparing, with unknowns in all positions, e.g., by using drawings and equations with a symbol for the unknown number to represent the problem.

Lesson Objective
Use bar models to represent a variety of addition and subtraction situations.

Essential Question
How are bar models used to show addition and subtraction problems?

Materials MathBoard

Digital Path

☑ **Animated Math Models**   iT *iTools*: Counters

GO **eStudent Edition**

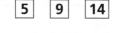

Daily Routines
Common Core
SPIRAL REVIEW

Problem of the Day
eTransparency **3.8**

Basic Facts
Write a subtraction fact using these three numbers. Then write a related addition fact.

5   9   14

Children may use their MathBoards to write the related number sentences.

If time permits, ask them to write a subtraction fact and a related addition fact for the numbers 7, 7, 14.

COMMON CORE
MATHEMATICAL PRACTICES
Using Bar Models for Comparison Subtraction

Children have used bar models to help them visualize addition and take-away subtraction problems. In this lesson they are introduced to bar models for comparison subtraction problems.

For comparison subtraction problems, two rows of bars are drawn. The top bar shows the larger amount in the comparison. The bottom bar shows the smaller amount. The bracketed area shows the unknown. As with the other bar models, children use these models to help them visualize how the known and unknown parts of a problem are related.

The bottom diagram shows a bar model for this comparison subtraction problem.

Emily buys 15 pears and 9 apples. How many more pears than apples does she buy?

• The larger amount is 15 pears and the smaller amount is 9 apples. So, children would subtract to find how many more pears than apples there are: 15 − 9 = 6.

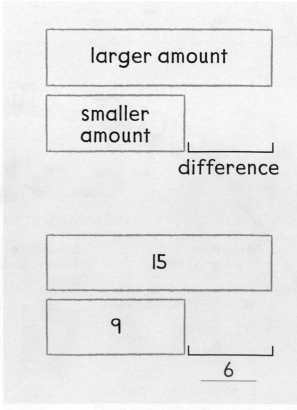

Differentiated Instruction Activities

ELL Language Support
🕐 Visual / Kinesthetic
Small Group

Strategy: Explore Context

Materials two-color counters

- Children need to identify and experience vocabulary in context to clarify the meaning of words.

- Write the following problem on the board and then read it aloud.

  Sara ate 6 grapes. Jake ate 4 grapes.
  How many more grapes did Sara eat than Jake?

- Have children model the problem. Discuss that the phrase *how many more* indicates they are comparing and can subtract to solve the problem.

See **ELL** Activity Guide for leveled activities.

Enrich
🕐 Visual
Individual / Partners

Materials Addition Fact Cards, Subtraction Fact Cards
(see *eTeacher Resources*)

- Have each child choose a fact card and write a word problem for the fact.

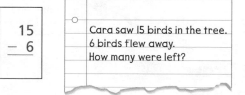

- Have partners solve each other's problems and then write another problem using the partner's fact card.

- Repeat with other fact cards. Have partners use both addition and subtraction cards during the activity.

RtI Response to Intervention

Reteach Tier 1
🕐 Visual / Kinesthetic
Whole Class / Small Group

Materials two-color counters

- Write these two problems on the board.

  Marla has 4 marbles. Jake has 9 marbles.
  How many marbles do they have in all?

  Sue has 13 books. She gives 4 books to Joe.
  How many books does Sue have left?

- Model the first problem as 4 red counters and 9 yellow counters. Describe that the red counters show Marla's marbles and the yellow counters show Jake's marbles. **The problem asks us to find how many marbles in all. So, we can add the groups to solve, 4 + 9 = 13.**

- For the second problem, model 13 with red counters. Ask: **What do these counters show?** the 13 books Sue has **How can we model Sue giving away 4 books?** Take away 4 counters. **Our model shows that Sue has 9 books left, 13 − 4 = 9.**

Tier 2
🕐 Visual / Kinesthetic
Small Group

Materials connecting cubes

- Write these two problems on the board.

  Jo has 4 apples and 3 pears. How many pieces of fruit does she have?

  Mark has 7 buttons. He gives 4 buttons to Carla. How many buttons does Mark have left?

- Read the first problem. Have children model the problem with 4 red and 3 green cubes. Explain that their cubes show Jo's 4 apples and 3 pears. Point out that the problem asks how many pieces of fruit Jo has in all. Ask: **How many cubes do you have in all?** 7 cubes **So, Jo has 7 pieces of fruit in all.**

- Read the second problem. Have children model the 7 buttons with red cubes. Ask: **How can you show the buttons Mark gives away?** Take away 4 cubes. **How many cubes are left?** 3 cubes **So, Mark has 3 buttons left.**

① ENGAGE GO Online · iTools

Materials *i*Tools: Counters

Access Prior Knowledge Use *i*Tools to show 3 blue bear counters and 8 red bear counters. Have children name the four related facts that can be represented by the bear counters. As children name the facts, have them write the facts on their MathBoards.

$3 + 8 = 11$, $8 + 3 = 11$, $11 - 8 = 3$, $11 - 3 = 8$

- **Suppose we take one of the red bear counters away. How would the related facts for the bears change?** Possible answer: The parts would be 7 and 3, and the whole would be 10.

② TEACH and TALK GO Online · Animated Math Models

▶ Listen and Draw REAL WORLD

Read this problem. Have children complete the first bar model to show the problem. Then have children write the number sentence to solve.

Hailey has 5 pennies in her pocket and 7 pennies in her wallet. How many pennies does she have?

- **What did you write in the two bars? Explain.** Possible answer: I wrote 5 and 7 because these bars show the two parts being combined.

- **What did you write below the bracket? Explain.** Possible answer: I wrote 12 because 12 pennies is the whole when I combine 5 pennies and 7 pennies.

- **What number sentence did you write? Explain.** Possible answer: I wrote $5 + 7 = 12$ to show that the parts are added together.

Repeat the activity for this problem. Have children complete the second bar model.

Blake has 12 pennies in his bank. He gives 5 pennies to his sister. How many pennies does he have now?

- **Why do the bar models for the two problems look the same?** Possible answer: The problems are related addition and subtraction problems. They have the same parts and the same whole.

Use **Math Talk** to focus on children's understanding of how addition and subtraction situations compare.

COMMON CORE · **CC.2.OA.1** Use addition and subtraction within 100 to solve one- and two-step word problems involving situations of adding to, taking from, putting together, taking apart, and comparing, with unknowns in all positions, e.g., by using drawings and equations with a symbol for the unknown number to represent the problem.

Name _____

Lesson 3.8

Algebra • Use Drawings to Represent Problems

COMMON CORE STANDARD CC.2.OA.1
Represent and solve problems involving addition and subtraction.

Essential Question How are bar models used to show addition and subtraction problems?

Listen and Draw REAL WORLD

Complete the bar model to show the problem.
Complete the number sentence to solve.

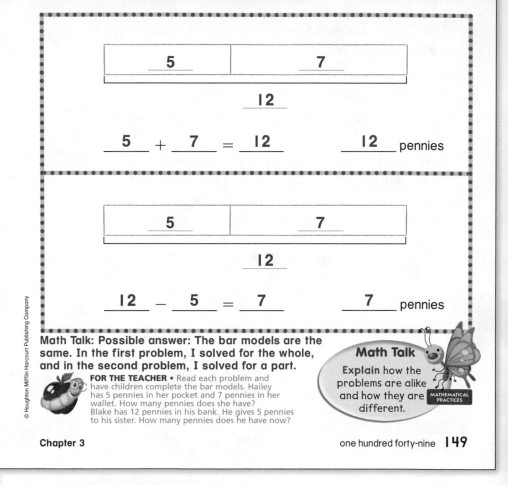

| 5 | 7 |

12

$\underline{\;5\;} + \underline{\;7\;} = \underline{\;12\;}$ $\underline{\;12\;}$ pennies

| 5 | 7 |

12

$\underline{\;12\;} - \underline{\;5\;} = \underline{\;7\;}$ $\underline{\;7\;}$ pennies

Math Talk: Possible answer: The bar models are the same. In the first problem, I solved for the whole, and in the second problem, I solved for a part.

FOR THE TEACHER • Read each problem and have children complete the bar models. Hailey has 5 pennies in her pocket and 7 pennies in her wallet. How many pennies does she have? Blake has 12 pennies in his bank. He gives 5 pennies to his sister. How many pennies does he have now?

Math Talk
Explain how the problems are alike and how they are different. MATHEMATICAL PRACTICES

Chapter 3

one hundred forty-nine **149**

© Houghton Mifflin Harcourt Publishing Company

Standards Practice 3.8

Common Core · SPIRAL REVIEW

Name _____

Lesson 3.8

Algebra • Use Drawings to Represent Problems

COMMON CORE STANDARD CC.2.OA.1
Represent and solve problems involving addition and subtraction.

Complete the bar model. Then write a number sentence to solve.

Possible number sentences are given.

1. Sara has 4 yellow beads and 3 green beads. How many beads does Sara have?

| 4 | 3 |

7

$\underline{4 + 3 = 7}$

$\underline{\;7\;}$ beads

2. Adam had 12 trucks. He gave 4 trucks to Ed. How many trucks does Adam have now?

| 8 | 4 |

12

$\underline{12 - 4 = 8}$

$\underline{\;8\;}$ trucks

3. Grandma has 14 red roses and 7 pink roses. How many more red roses than pink roses does she have?

| 14 |

| 7 | |

$\underline{14 - 7 = 7}$

$\underline{\;7\;}$

$\underline{\;7\;}$ more red roses

Chapter 3

sixty-seven **P67**

Lesson Check (CC.2.OA.1)

★ TEST PREP

1. Abby has 16 grapes. Jason has 9 grapes. How many more grapes does Abby have than Jason?

| 16 |

| 9 |

___

- ● 7
- ○ 8
- ○ 15
- ○ 25

Spiral Review (CC.2.OA.2, CC.2.NBT.3)

2. Which has the same difference as $16 - 7$? (Lesson 3.7)

- ○ $10 - 10$
- ○ $10 - 6$
- ○ $10 - 7$
- ● $10 - 1$

3. What is the difference? (Lesson 3.6)

$18 - 9 = $ ___

- ○ 6
- ● 9
- ○ 10
- ○ 27

4. Which is another way to write $300 + 20 + 5$? (Lesson 2.7)

- ○ 55
- ○ 235
- ● 325
- ○ 523

5. What is the value of the underlined digit? (Lesson 1.5)

2**8**

- ○ 80
- ● 20
- ○ 10
- ○ 2

P68 sixty-eight

Model and Draw

You can use bar models to show problems.

Ben eats 14 crackers. Ron eats 6 crackers. How many more crackers does Ben eat than Ron?

14

6	
	8

$14 - 6 = 8$

___8___ more crackers

Suzy had 14 cookies. She gave 6 cookies to Grace. How many cookies does Suzy have now?

6	8
14	

$14 - 6 = 8$

___8___ cookies

Share and Show 🖊️ Math Board

Complete the bar model. Then write a number sentence to solve.

Possible number sentences are given.

✓1. Mr. James bought 15 plain bagels and 9 raisin bagels. How many more plain bagels than raisin bagels did he buy?

15

9	
	6

$15 - 9 = 6$

___6___ more plain bagels

150 one hundred fifty

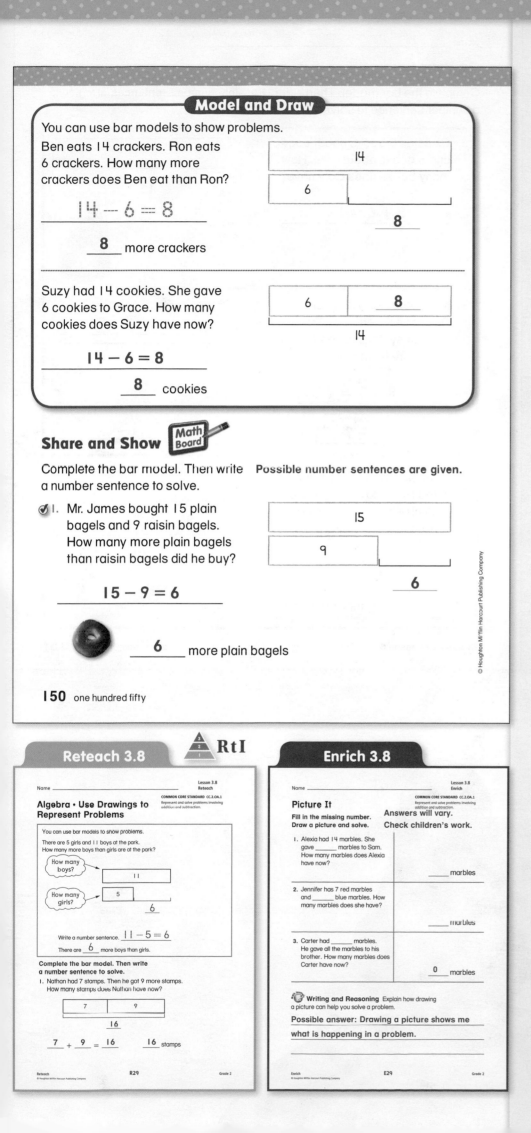

Name _____ Lesson 3.8 Reteach

Algebra • Use Drawings to Represent Problems

COMMON CORE STANDARD CC.2.OA.1
Represent and solve problems involving addition and subtraction.

You can use bar models to show problems.

There are 5 girls and 11 boys at the park. How many more boys than girls are at the park?

(How many boys?) → [11]

(How many girls?) → [5] [6]

Write a number sentence. $11 - 5 = 6$

There are __6__ more boys than girls.

Complete the bar model. Then write a number sentence to solve.

1. Nathan had 7 stamps. Then he got 9 more stamps. How many stamps does Nathan have now?

7	9
16	

$7 + 9 = 16$ __16__ stamps

Reteach R29 Grade 2
© Houghton Mifflin Harcourt Publishing Company

Enrich 3.8

Name _____ Lesson 3.8 Enrich

Picture It

Fill in the missing number. Draw a picture and solve.

Answers will vary. Check children's work.

COMMON CORE STANDARD CC.2.OA.1
Represent and solve problems involving addition and subtraction.

1. Alexia had 14 marbles. She gave _____ marbles to Sam. How many marbles does Alexia have now?

_____ marbles

2. Jennifer has 7 red marbles and _____ blue marbles. How many marbles does she have?

_____ marbles

3. Carter had _____ marbles. He gave all the marbles to his brother. How many marbles does Carter have now?

__0__ marbles

✏️ **Writing and Reasoning** Explain how drawing a picture can help you solve a problem.

Possible answer: Drawing a picture shows me

what is happening in a problem.

_____

Enrich E29 Grade 2
© Houghton Mifflin Harcourt Publishing Company

▶ Model and Draw 〔MATHEMATICAL PRACTICES〕

Work through the models with children. Have volunteers restate the two subtraction problems in their own words. Discuss that the first problem is a comparison subtraction problem and the second problem is a take-away subtraction problem.

- **How are the two subtraction problems different?** Possible answer: In the first problem, two groups of crackers are being compared. In the second problem, 6 cookies are taken away from 14 cookies.

Then talk with children about how the bar models for the take-away subtraction and the comparison subtraction are different even though the subtraction sentences are the same.

③ PRACTICE 〔Math Board〕

▶ Share and Show • Guided Practice

Exercise 1 connects to the learning model.

- **In Exercise 1, how did you decide how to complete the bar model?** Possible answer: I wrote 6 under the bracket since the bar model shows that Mr. James bought 6 fewer raisin bagels than plain bagels.

Use Exercise 1 for **Quick Check**. Children should use their MathBoards to show their solution to this exercise.

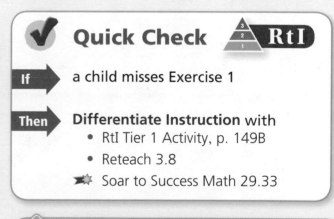

✔️ **Quick Check** 🔺 **RtI**

If ➤ a child misses Exercise 1

Then ➤ **Differentiate Instruction** with
- RtI Tier 1 Activity, p. 149B
- Reteach 3.8
- 🌟 Soar to Success Math 29.33

⚠️ **COMMON ERRORS**

Error Children do not understand the bar model for a comparison subtraction problem.

Example Children incorrectly label the bar model in Exercise 1.

Springboard to Learning Children may not understand the representation found in a comparison bar model. Explain that you need two bars, one for each amount. The two bars are lined up so you can see how they compare. You may want to ask children to use trains of connecting cubes to model the comparison in a more concrete way.

Lesson 3.8   150

▶ On Your Own • Independent Practice

If children answer Exercise 1 correctly, assign Exercises 2–4.

Go Deeper 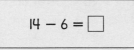 MATHEMATICAL PRACTICES

Write a subtraction fact on the board.

$$14 - 6 = \boxed{}$$

First ask children to tell or write take-away subtraction story problems that could be solved by using the fact. Then ask them to tell or write comparison subtraction story problems that could be solved by using the fact.

Have children work in pairs and draw bar models for their story problems. Ask children to share their bar models and explain how their models show their story problems.

Name _____

On Your Own

Complete the bar model. Then write a number sentence to solve.   **Possible number sentences are given.**

2. Cole has 5 books about dogs and 6 books about cats. How many books does Cole have?

| 5 | 6 |

11

$$\underline{5 + 6 = 11}$$

__11__ books

3. Miss Gore had 18 pencils. She gave 9 pencils to Erin. How many pencils does Miss Gore have now?

| 9 | 9 |

18

$$\underline{18 - 9 = 9}$$

__9__ pencils

4. Anne has 16 blue clips and 9 red clips. How many more blue clips than red clips does she have?

| 16 |

| 9 |

7

$$\underline{16 - 9 = 7}$$

__7__ more blue clips

© Houghton Mifflin Harcourt Publishing Company

PROBLEM SOLVING

REAL WORLD — Write Math

Use the information in the table to solve. Write or draw to explain.

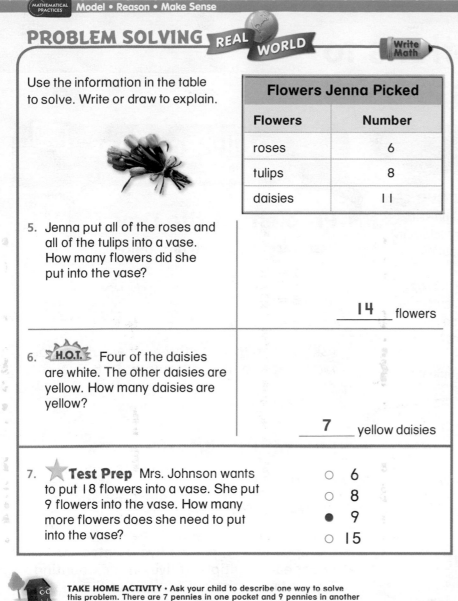

Flowers Jenna Picked	
Flowers	**Number**
roses	6
tulips	8
daisies	11

5. Jenna put all of the roses and all of the tulips into a vase. How many flowers did she put into the vase?

____14____ flowers

6. **H.O.T.** Four of the daisies are white. The other daisies are yellow. How many daisies are yellow?

____7____ yellow daisies

7. ⭐ **Test Prep** Mrs. Johnson wants to put 18 flowers into a vase. She put 9 flowers into the vase. How many more flowers does she need to put into the vase?

- ○ 6
- ○ 8
- ● 9
- ○ 15

🏠 **TAKE HOME ACTIVITY** • Ask your child to describe one way to solve this problem. There are 7 pennies in one pocket and 9 pennies in another pocket. How many pennies are there?

152 one hundred fifty-two

© Houghton Mifflin Harcourt Publishing Company

FOR MORE PRACTICE:
Standards Practice Book, pp. P67–P68

▶ **Problem Solving** (MATHEMATICAL PRACTICES)

Unlock the Problem A key to solving Exercise 5 is understanding how to find the needed information in the table.

H.O.T. Problem For Exercise 6, children use information found in the table and in the problem to solve the problem.

⭐ **Test Prep Coach**

Test Prep Coach helps teachers to identify common errors that children can make.

In Exercise 7, if children selected:

- **6,** they do not know the doubles facts.
- **8,** they subtracted incorrectly.
- **15,** they chose a number in between 9 and 18.

4 SUMMARIZE (MATHEMATICAL PRACTICES)

Essential Question

How are bar models used to show addition and subtraction problems?
Possible answer: Bar models show the parts and whole that I know and help me know what is missing.

Math Journal

Explain how you decided how to label the bar model in Exercise 4 on page 151.

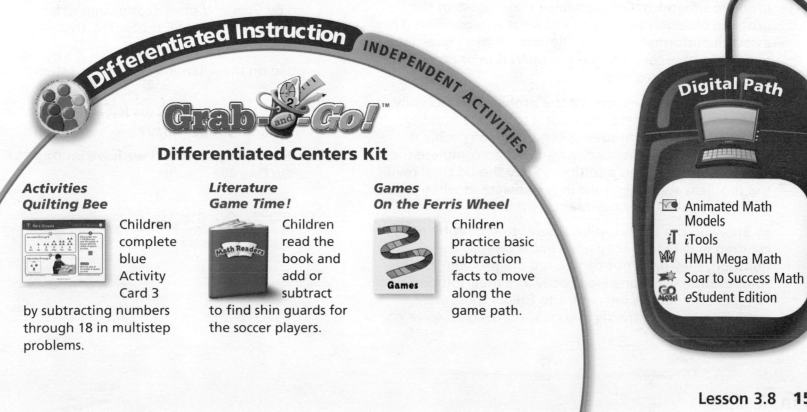

Differentiated Instruction — INDEPENDENT ACTIVITIES

Grab-and-Go!™

Differentiated Centers Kit

Activities
Quilting Bee

Children complete blue Activity Card 3 by subtracting numbers through 18 in multistep problems.

Literature
Game Time!

Children read the book and add or subtract to find shin guards for the soccer players.

Games
On the Ferris Wheel

Children practice basic subtraction facts to move along the game path.

Digital Path

- 📺 Animated Math Models
- *i*T *i*Tools
- 〽️ HMH Mega Math
- Soar to Success Math
- 🔵 *e*Student Edition

Lesson 3.8 152

Algebra • Use Equations to Represent Problems

LESSON AT A GLANCE

Common Core Standard
Represent and solve problems involving addition and subtraction. CC.2.OA.1 Use addition and subtraction within 100 to solve one- and two-step word problems involving situations of adding to, taking from, putting together, taking apart, and comparing, with unknowns in all positions, e.g., by using drawings and equations with a symbol for the unknown number to represent the problem.

Lesson Objective
Write equations to represent and solve a variety of addition and subtraction situations.

Essential Question
How are number sentences used to show addition and subtraction situations?

Materials MathBoard

Digital Path

☑ Animated Math Models

𝕄𝕄 HMH Mega Math

𝑖T *i*Tools: Counters

📱 eStudent Edition

COMMON CORE PROFESSIONAL DEVELOPMENT

Building Mathematical Practices

CC.K–12.MP.2 Reason abstractly and quantitatively.

In this lesson, children use number sentences to represent problem situations. Children must make sense of the problem situation to understand what is happening. They assess the information given, determine what question is to be answered, and choose the operation or process to use to solve the problem.

Then children must represent the problem symbolically. One way to represent a problem is to write a number sentence. A number sentence organizes the problem situation in a mathematical way. Children complete the computation and find a solution. They should then revisit the problem and make sure they understand what their mathematical answer represents within the problem.

By applying the quantitative answer to the problem, children may realize they have not answered the question, they have not completed the problem, or their computation was done incorrectly and their solution does not make sense. It is important to follow these steps, reasoning both abstractly and quantitatively to solve problems.

Daily Routines

Math Board

SPIRAL REVIEW

Problem of the Day

eTransparency
3.9

Basic Facts Find each difference.

15 − 7 = _____ 8

14 − 8 = _____ 6

13 − 6 = _____ 7

Ask children to write three other subtraction facts that also have differences of 8, 6, and 7.

Fluency Builder

Counting Tape

Materials Counting Tape

EVERY DAY COUNTS ®

When you reach Day 30, to accent the multiples of five, place a five-pointed star under each multiple of five on the Counting Tape. Mark each new multiple of five in the same way.

On some days, have the class count the days on the Tape by fives. On other days count by tens, clapping on the last ten and then count on by fives and ones. (For example, ten, twenty, thirty (clap), thirty-five, thirty-six, thirty-seven.)

Build on these landmarks with questions such as:

- **How many stars do we have on the Counting Tape today?**

- **How many stars will we have on Day 35? On Day 40?**

Differentiated Instruction Activities

ELL Language Support
Kinesthetic / Visual · Small Group

Strategy: Explore Context

Materials two-color counters

- Children need to identify and experience vocabulary in context to clarify the meanings of words.

- Write the following problem on the board. Then read it aloud.

  There were 6 toys in a box. Some toys were taken out. There were 4 toys left in the box. How many toys were taken out? 2 toys

- Have children draw a picture to model the problem to help them understand that since some toys were removed, they need to subtract to solve the problem.

See **ELL** Activity Guide for leveled activities.

Enrich
Visual · Individual / Partners

- Ask each child to write an addition or subtraction story problem involving the number 8.

  > There were 11 apples on a tree. Some apples fell off. There are 8 apples left on the tree. How many apples fell off?

- Have partners trade problems. Ask each child to draw a diagram or picture that might help him or her solve the problem.

- Have children write a number sentence that could be used to solve the problem. Then have them solve.

- Have children discuss with their partners how they solved each other's problems.

RtI Response to Intervention

Reteach Tier 1
Kinesthetic / Visual · Whole Class / Small Group

Materials connecting cubes

- Write this problem on the board.

  Olivia has 12 stickers. She gives 5 stickers to Anna. How many stickers does Olivia have now?

- Read the problem aloud. Make a 12-cube train to model the stickers Olivia starts with. Write *12* on the board. Count 5 cubes from one end of the cube train and remove them. Explain that the removed cubes model the 5 stickers Olivia gave to Anna. Write − *5* next to 12.

- Show the remaining cubes. Discuss that these cubes model the stickers Olivia has now. Count the cubes with children. Then write = *7* after 12 − 5. Have children explain in their own words how the number sentence shows the problem.

Tier 2
Visual / Kinesthetic · Small Group

Materials connecting cubes

- Write the following problem on the board.

  Esteban has 9 connecting cubes. He gives 4 cubes to Van. How many cubes does Esteban have now?

- Have each child count 9 connecting cubes and make a cube train.

- Ask: **Are cubes being added together or are cubes being taken away?** Cubes are being taken away. Guide children to act out the problem by removing 4 cubes from the cube train of 9 cubes.

- Write the subtraction sentence 9 − 4 = 5 on the board. Explain that the model children made represents this subtraction problem because it shows how some of the cubes are taken away from the whole group.

1 ENGAGE 📋 Math Board

Access Prior Knowledge On the board, write the following:

_____ + _____ = 10

10 − _____ = _____

- **What pair of numbers can you use in both number sentences?** Possible answers: 5 and 5; 6 and 4; 1 and 9

2 TEACH and TALK 🔵 GO Online · Animated Math Models

▶ Listen and Draw 🌎 REAL WORLD

Read the directions aloud.

- **What are you asked to do?** write a story problem that can be solved using the bar model

- **How can you use this bar model to decide what kind of story problem to write?**
Possible answer: I can look at the bar model and know what number is the whole and what number is one part. Then I can use this information to decide if I will write an addition or a subtraction story problem.

Ask for a volunteer to read his or her story problem to the class. Ask children to describe how the bar model helps show the story problem. Then ask for additional volunteers to read their story problems and discuss them with the class.

Use Math Talk to focus on children's understanding of how to decide whether to use addition or subtraction based on the situation.

CC.2.OA.1 Use addition and subtraction within 100 to solve one- and two-step word problems involving situations of adding to, taking from, putting together, taking apart, and comparing, with unknowns in all positions, e.g., by using drawings and equations with a symbol for the unknown number to represent the problem.

COMMON CORE

Name _____

Lesson 3.9

Algebra • Use Equations to Represent Problems

COMMON CORE STANDARD CC.2.OA.1
Represent and solve problems involving addition and subtraction.

Essential Question How are number sentences used to show addition and subtraction situations?

Listen and Draw 🌎 REAL WORLD

Write a story problem that could be solved using this bar model.

	9

15

Story problems will vary. One possible problem: Kaley had some marbles. Her brother gave her 9 more marbles. Now she has 15 marbles. How many marbles did Kaley have to start?

Math Talk: Possible answer: I would subtract. I know the total is 15 marbles, and I need to find the number of marbles that is added to 9 marbles to have 15 marbles in all.

Math Talk
Would you add or subtract to solve your story problem? Explain.
MATHEMATICAL PRACTICES

🐛 **FOR THE TEACHER** • Discuss with children how this bar model can be used to represent an addition or a subtraction situation.

Chapter 3

one hundred fifty-three **153**

© Houghton Mifflin Harcourt Publishing Company

Standards Practice 3.9

Common Core

SPIRAL REVIEW

Name _____

Lesson 3.9

Algebra • Use Equations to Represent Problems

COMMON CORE STANDARD CC.2.OA.1
Represent and solve problems involving addition and subtraction.

Possible number sententences are given.

Write a number sentence for the problem. Use a ⬛ for the missing number. Then solve.

1. There were 15 apples in a bowl. Dan used some apples to make a pie. Now there are 7 apples in the bowl. How many apples did Dan use?

$15 − ⬛ = 7$

__8__ apples

2. Amy has 16 gift bags. She fills 8 gift bags with whistles. How many gift bags are not filled with whistles?

$16 − 8 = ⬛$

__8__ gift bags

3. There were 5 dogs at the park. Then 9 more dogs joined them. How many dogs are at the park now?

$5 + 9 = ⬛$

__14__ dogs

PROBLEM SOLVING 🌎 REAL WORLD

Write or draw to show how you solved the problem.

4. Tony has 7 blue cubes and 6 red cubes. How many cubes does he have in all?

__13__ cubes

Chapter 3

sixty-nine **P69**

Lesson Check (CC.2.OA.1)

⭐ TEST PREP

1. Fred peeled 9 carrots. Nancy peeled 6 carrots. How many fewer carrots did Nancy peel than Fred?

- ○ 15
- ○ 6
- ● 3
- ○ 2

2. Omar has 8 marbles. Joy has 7 marbles. How many marbles do they have in all?

- ○ 1
- ○ 5
- ○ 8
- ● 15

Spiral Review (CC.2.OA.2, CC.2.NBT.1)

3. What is the sum? (Lesson 3.1)

$7 + 8 = ?$

- ○ 2
- ○ 7
- ● 15
- ○ 17

4. What is the sum? (Lesson 1.4)

$5 + 4 + 3 = \_\_\_\_$

- ● 12
- ○ 15
- ○ 18
- ○ 19

5. Which has the same value as 1 hundred 7 tens? (Lesson 2.2)

- ○ 70 tens
- ● 17 tens
- ○ 10 tens
- ○ 7 tens

6. Which of the following is a way to describe the number 358? (Lesson 2.4)

- ○ 8 hundreds 5 tens 3 ones
- ○ 5 hundreds 3 tens 8 ones
- ○ 3 hundreds 8 tens 5 ones
- ● 3 hundreds 5 tens 8 ones

P70 seventy

Model and Draw

A number sentence can be used to show a problem.

There were some girls and 4 boys at the playground. There were 9 children in all. How many girls were at the playground?

$$\blacksquare + 4 = 9$$

> The $\blacksquare$ is a placeholder for the missing number.

Think: $5 + 4 = 9$

So, there were ___5___ girls at the playground.

Share and Show

Write a number sentence for the problem. Use a $\blacksquare$ for the missing number. Then solve.

Possible number sentences are given.

1. There were 14 ants on the sidewalk. Then 6 ants went into the grass. How many ants were still on the sidewalk?

   $$14 - 6 = \blacksquare$$

   ___8___ ants

2. There were 7 big dogs and 4 little dogs at the park. How many dogs were at the park?

   $$7 + 4 = \blacksquare$$

   ___11___ dogs

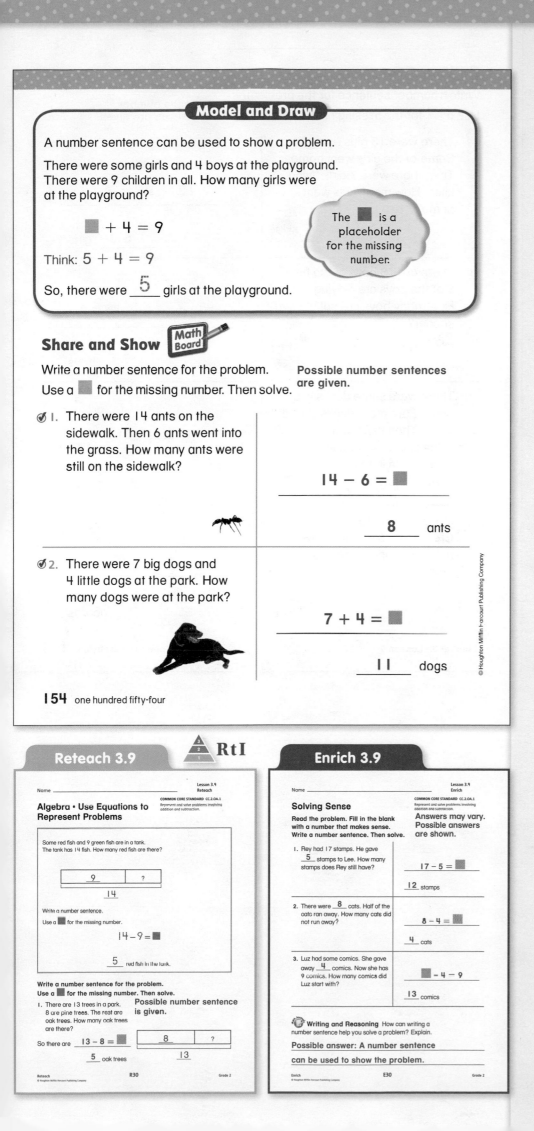

© Houghton Mifflin Harcourt Publishing Company

Model and Draw

Work through the model with children. Explain that the gray box represents an unknown number.

- **Look at the number sentence with the gray box. How does this number sentence show the problem?** Possible answer: The gray box stands for the number of girls, and 4 is added to this amount because that is the number of boys. The sum, 9, is the number of children in all.

- **Could a subtraction sentence also be used to show the problem? Explain.** Yes; Possible answer: I could subtract 4 from 9 to find how many children are girls.

3 PRACTICE

▶ Share and Show • Guided Practice

Exercises 1–2 connect to the learning model. For some of the exercises, children may write a subtraction or an addition sentence.

- **In Exercise 1, what number sentence did you write? Explain.** Possible answer: I wrote $14 = 6 + \blacksquare$. I know that there were 14 ants and that 6 ants left.

Use Exercises 1 and 2 for **Quick Check**. Children should use their MathBoards to show their solutions to these exercises.

✔ Quick Check · RtI

If → a child misses Exercises 1 and 2

Then → **Differentiate Instruction** with
- RtI Tier 1 Activity, p. 153B
- Reteach 3.9
- Soar to Success Math 11.17

⚠ COMMON ERRORS

Error Children may write an incorrect number sentence for a problem.

Example In Exercise 2, children write $7 - 4 = 3$.

Springboard to Learning Have children draw a picture or diagram to model the problem. Then have children describe in their own words what the problem is about.

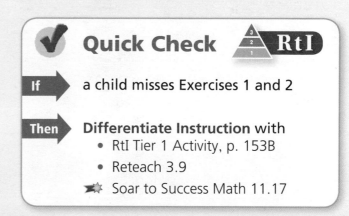

▶ On Your Own • Independent Practice

If children answer Exercises 1 and 2 correctly, assign Exercises 3–6. Remind children that some of the story problems may be solved with an addition or subtraction number sentence.

Go Deeper

To extend their thinking, challenge children to choose one of the exercises on this page and write a new story problem by changing the action in the story so that they would solve the problem in a different way. Encourage children to share their story problems and number sentences with the class.

Name _____

On Your Own

Write a number sentence for the problem. Use a ▇ for the missing number. Then solve.

Possible number sentences are given.

3. There were 13 girls flying kites. Some of the girls went home. Then there were 7 girls flying kites. How many girls went home?

$$13 - ▇ = 7$$

____6____ girls

4. There are 18 boys at the field. 9 of the boys are playing soccer. How many boys are not playing soccer?

$$18 - 9 = ▇$$

____9____ boys

5. There were some ducks in a pond. Four more ducks joined them. Then there were 12 ducks in the pond. How many ducks were in the pond at first?

$$▇ + 4 = 12$$

____8____ ducks

6. Matthew found 9 acorns. Greg found 6 acorns. How many acorns did the two boys find?

$$9 + 6 = ▇$$

____15____ acorns

PROBLEM SOLVING REAL WORLD

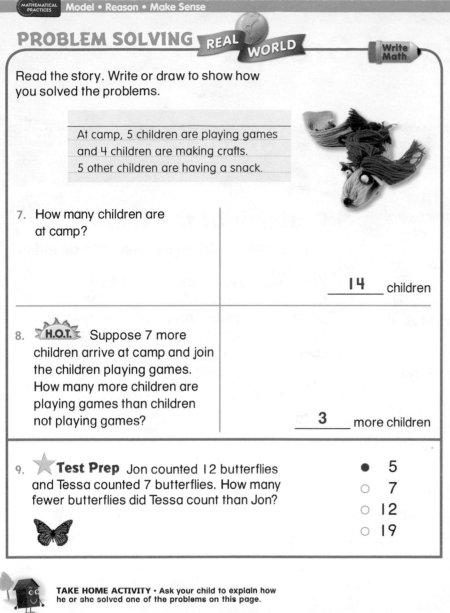

Read the story. Write or draw to show how you solved the problems.

> At camp, 5 children are playing games and 4 children are making crafts. 5 other children are having a snack.

7. How many children are at camp?

_____14_____ children

8. **H.O.T.** Suppose 7 more children arrive at camp and join the children playing games. How many more children are playing games than children not playing games?

_____3_____ more children

9. ⭐ **Test Prep** Jon counted 12 butterflies and Tessa counted 7 butterflies. How many fewer butterflies did Tessa count than Jon?

- ● 5
- ○ 7
- ○ 12
- ○ 19

TAKE HOME ACTIVITY • Ask your child to explain how he or she solved one of the problems on this page.

156 one hundred fifty-six

FOR EXTRA PRACTICE:
Standards Practice Book, p. P76

FOR MORE PRACTICE:
Standards Practice Book, pp. P69–P70

▶ **Problem Solving**

Have children read the story.

H.O.T. Problem Exercise 8 requires children to use higher order thinking skills to solve a multistep problem. They use information found at the top of the page and in the exercise to solve.

⭐ **Test Prep Coach**

Test Prep Coach helps teachers to identify common errors that children can make.

In Exercise 9, if children selected:

- **7,** they chose the number of butterflies Tessa counted.
- **12,** they chose the number of butterflies Jon counted.
- **19,** they found the sum of the butterflies counted.

4 SUMMARIZE

Essential Question

How are number sentences used to show addition and subtraction situations?
Possible answer: Number sentences show what is happening in the situation.

Math Journal

Write a story problem for the addition sentence 7 + ▮ = 9. Solve the story problem.

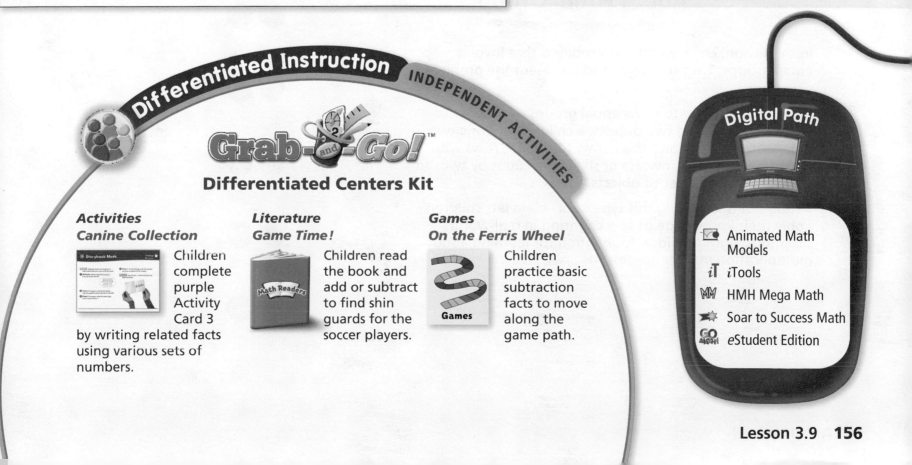

Differentiated Instruction — **INDEPENDENT ACTIVITIES**

Grab-and-Go!™
Differentiated Centers Kit

Activities
Canine Collection

Children complete purple Activity Card 3 by writing related facts using various sets of numbers.

Literature
Game Time!

Children read the book and add or subtract to find shin guards for the soccer players.

Games
On the Ferris Wheel

Children practice basic subtraction facts to move along the game path.

Digital Path

- 📺 Animated Math Models
- *iT* *i*Tools
- MM HMH Mega Math
- 📖 Soar to Success Math
- GO MATH *e*Student Edition

Problem Solving • Equal Groups

Common Core Standard

Work with equal groups of objects to gain foundations for multiplication. **CC.2.OA.4** Use addition to find the total number of objects arranged in rectangular arrays with up to 5 rows and up to 5 columns; write an equation to express the total as a sum of equal addends.

Lesson Objective

Solve problems involving equal groups by using the strategy *act it out*.

Essential Question

How can acting it out help when solving a problem about equal groups?

Materials MathBoard, two-color counters

Digital Path

 **HMH Mega Math**   **eStudent Edition**

Problem of the Day

eTransparency **3.10**

Calendar Math   Count by fives on a calendar.

CALENDAR   Have children count by fives, starting with 5. Invite them to circle each number on a calendar as they count. Ask them to describe any patterns they see. Possible answer: Every fifth number is circled.

COMMON CORE PROFESSIONAL DEVELOPMENT

Acting Out Problems About Equal Groups

In this lesson, children act out problems that involve equal groups. They use objects to represent the problem situations.

Children may draw to show equal groups of objects. To show five groups of two objects, a child could draw two objects in one row, and then draw four more rows with two objects in each row. He or she could count by twos to find the total number of objects.

Acting out and solving this type of problem lets children apply their knowledge of skip counting in real-world situations. It also builds a foundation for learning about multiplication in later grades.

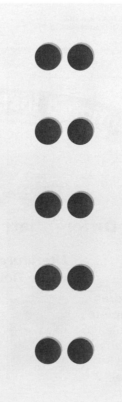

Differentiated Instruction Activities

ELL Language Support
Auditory / Visual
Small Group

Strategy: Draw

Materials crayons

- Children can demonstrate their understanding of story problems by drawing a picture.

- Read the story problem. **There are 5 flowers in each window box. How many flowers are there in 2 window boxes?**

- Have children draw to solve the story problem.

See ELL Activity Guide for leveled activities.

Enrich
Visual / Linguistic
Individual / Partners

Materials posterboard, two-color counters, markers

- Distribute art supplies and tell children that they will be making a poster showing how to act out and solve a problem.

- Direct children to write a story problem that involves finding how many objects there are altogether in a certain number of equal groups.

- Have children act out the problem using counters to model equal groups in rows.

- Have them make a poster that shows the problem and the steps they used to act it out.

RtI Response to Intervention

Reteach Tier 1
Visual / Kinesthetic
Whole Class / Small Group

Materials two-color counters

- Write this problem on the board and read it aloud.

  Mrs. Bronson has some counters in 3 rows. She has 4 counters in each row. How many counters does she have?

- Help children model the problem using counters.

- **How many rows of counters does Mrs. Bronson have?** 3 rows **How many rows of counters should you make?** 3 rows

- **How many counters does Mrs. Bronson have in each row?** 4 counters **How many counters should you put in each row?** 4 counters Have children make 3 rows with 4 counters in each row.

- **We have 3 rows of 4 counters. Now skip count by fours to find how many counters there are in all.** Have children point to each row as they skip count. 4, 8, 12; Mrs. Bronson has 12 counters.

Tier 2
Visual / Kinesthetic
Small Group

Materials connecting cubes

- Write this problem on the board and read it aloud.

  Ms. Jane has 3 rows of cubes. Each row has 2 cubes. How many cubes does she have?

- Show children 3 rows of cubes with 2 cubes in each row.

- Review with children what a row is. Have children point to a row of cubes. **How many rows of cubes are there?** 3 rows **How many cubes are in each row?** 2 cubes Explain that this model shows the cubes that Ms. Jane has.

- Guide children to skip count by twos to find the total number of cubes in the model. 2, 4, 6; 6 cubes

- You may wish to have children count the cubes by ones to check their answer.

1 ENGAGE

Access Prior Knowledge Discuss with children examples of when they might use skip counting to find a total number of objects in several equal groups.

- **What are some items you might see in equal groups in a store?** Possible answer: 2 bars of soap in a package

- **Describe how you could count to find how many bars of soap there are in 4 packages of 2 bars of soap.** 2, 4, 6, 8; I counted by twos until I said four numbers. There are 8 bars of soap in 4 packages.

2 TEACH and TALK

HMH Mega Math

▶ Unlock the Problem

Materials two-color counters

After reading the problem with children, work through the Problem Solving Graphic Organizer together.

- **What are you asked to find?** how many stickers Theo has

- **What information do you need to use?** He puts stickers in 5 rows. There are 3 stickers in each row.

- **How can you use the strategy act it out to solve this problem?** Possible answer: I can use counters to stand for the stickers. I can use 5 rows of counters with 3 counters in each row.

Have children use the counters to act out the problem to make rows with equal groups of counters. Then have them draw a picture of their rows of counters to show their work.

- **How can skip counting help you find the solution?** Possible answer: The counters can help me skip count by threes to find the total number of stickers: 3, 6, 9, 12, 15.

Have children answer the question in the problem. Theo has 15 stickers.

COMMON CORE

CC.2.OA.4 Use addition to find the total number of objects arranged in rectangular arrays with up to 5 rows and up to 5 columns; write an equation to express the total as a sum of equal addends.

Name _____

Problem Solving • Equal Groups

Essential Question How can acting it out help when solving a problem about equal groups?

COMMON CORE STANDARD CC.2.OA.4
Work with equal groups of objects to gain foundations for multiplication.

Theo puts his stickers in 5 rows.
There are 3 stickers in each row.
How many stickers does Theo have?

? Unlock the Problem

What do I need to find?	**What information do I need to use?**
how many stickers Theo has	__5 rows__ of stickers __3 stickers__ in each row

Show how to solve the problem.

Check children's work.

HOME CONNECTION · Your child used counters to act out the problem. Counters are a concrete tool that helps children act out the problem.

© Houghton Mifflin Harcourt Publishing Company

Chapter 3   one hundred fifty-seven **157**

Standards Practice 3.10

Common Core   SPIRAL REVIE

Name _____

Problem Solving • Equal Groups

PROBLEM SOLVING
Lesson 3.10

COMMON CORE STANDARD CC.2.OA.4
Work with equal groups of objects to gain foundations for multiplication.

**Act out the problem.
Draw to show what you did.** **Check children's work.**

1. Mr. Anderson has 4 plates of cookies. There are 5 cookies on each plate. How many cookies are there in all?

__20__ cookies

2. Ms. Trane puts some stickers in 3 rows. There are 2 stickers in each row. How many stickers does Ms. Trane have?

__6__ stickers

3. There are 5 books in each box. How many books are in 5 boxes?

__25__ books

Lesson Check (CC.2.OA.4)

★TEST PREP

1. Jaime puts 3 oranges on each tray. How many oranges are on 5 trays?
   - ○ 8
   - ● 15
   - ○ 35
   - ○ 53

2. Maurice has 4 rows of toys with 4 toys in each row. How many toys does he have in all?
   - ○ 4
   - ○ 8
   - ● 16
   - ○ 20

Spiral Review (CC.2.OA.1, CC.2.OA.2, CC.2.OA.3)

3. Jack has 12 pencils and 7 pens. How many more pencils than pens does he have? (Lesson 3.8)
   - ○ 19
   - ○ 9
   - ○ 6
   - ● 5

4. Laura has 9 apples. Jon has 6 apples. How many apples do they have in all? (Lesson 3.9)
   - ○ 3
   - ○ 12
   - ● 15
   - ○ 16

5. Which of these is an even number? (Lesson 1.1)
   - ○ 1
   - ○ 3
   - ○ 5
   - ● 8

6. What is the sum? (Lesson 3.2)

   $7 + 9 = $ ___
   - ● 16
   - ○ 17
   - ○ 18
   - ○ 19

Chapter 3   seventy-one **P71**

P72 seventy-two

Try Another Problem

Act out the problem.
Draw to show what you did.

> • What do I need to find?
> • What information do I need to use?

1. Maria puts all of her postcards in 4 rows. There are 3 postcards in each row. How many postcards does Maria have?

   __12__ postcards

   Check children's drawings.

2. Jamal puts 4 toys in each box. How many toys will he put in 4 boxes?

   __16__ toys

   Check children's drawings.

Math Talk
Explain how acting it out and skip counting helped you solve the second problem.

Math Talk: Possible answer: Acting it out helped me skip count by fours to find the total number of toys: 4, 8, 12, 16.

Use questions to guide children through Exercise 1. As children draw to show their work, remind them to show equal groups in equal rows in their pictures.

- **What do you need to find?** how many postcards Maria has

- **What information do you need to use?** She puts all of her postcards in 4 rows. There are 3 postcards in each row.

- **How can you act out this problem to find the number of postcards Maria has?** Possible answer: I can act it out by showing 4 rows of counters with 3 counters in each row.

- **How does using counters help you find the total number of postcards?** Possible answer: It shows the pattern of 4 equal groups of 3. So, to find the total number of postcards, I can skip count by threes: 3, 6, 9, 12. She has 12 postcards.

- **How do you know that your answer makes sense?** Accept reasonable answers that demonstrate children's understanding of acting out a problem and skip counting.

Repeat with a similar discussion for the second problem.

Use **Math Talk** to focus on children's understanding of how to represent equal groups and skip count to solve a problem.

Portfolio You may suggest that children place a completed Try Another Problem in their portfolios.

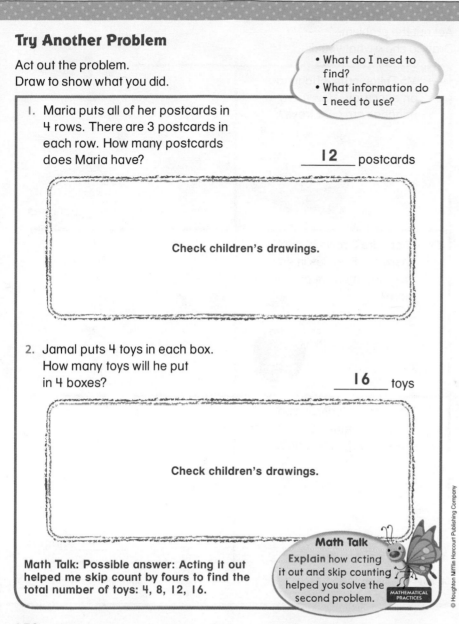

Reteach 3.10 △ RtI

Name _____
Lesson 3.10 Reteach

Problem Solving • Equal Groups

COMMON CORE STANDARD CC.2.OA.4
Work with equal groups of objects to gain foundations for multiplication.

Clarence puts grapes in 4 rows.
He puts 5 grapes in each row
How many grapes does Clarence have?

Unlock the Problem

What do I need to find?	What information do I need to use?
how many grapes	Clarence has __4__ rows of grapes.
Clarence has	He puts __5__ grapes in each row.

Show how to solve the problem.

Clarence has __20__ grapes.

Draw to show what you did.

1. Rachel puts her markers in 3 rows.
   Each row has 3 markers.
   How many markers does Rachel have?

   Check children's drawings.

   Rachel has __9__ markers.

Reteach   R31   Grade 2

Enrich 3.10

Name _____
Lesson 3.10 Enrich

Sorting Stickers

COMMON CORE STANDARD CC.2.OA.4
Work with equal groups of objects to gain foundations for multiplication.

Jamal's stickers need to be organized. Each type of sticker must be grouped together. Different types of stickers cannot be on the same page. Each page can fit 2 rows of 3 stickers.
Draw a diagram to show the pages.

1. How many pages do you need for ♡?	1 page; Check children's work.
2. How many pages do you need for ☺?	1 page; Check children's work.
3. How many pages do you need for ☆?	3 pages; Check children's work.
4. How many pages do you need for ☾?	1 page; Check children's work.

Writing and Reasoning How many rows of 3 stickers can Jamal make in all? Write the counting pattern to show the total.

10 rows

3, 6, 9, 12, 15, 18, 21, 24, 27, 30

Enrich   E31   Grade 2

⚠ **COMMON ERRORS**

Error Children may not see the relationship between the pattern of equal groups and skip counting.

Example In Exercise 1, children may act out the problem correctly (4 groups of 3), but not realize that they can skip count to find the total number of postcards.

Springboard to Learning Demonstrate how skip counting is just a faster way to count objects in equal groups. Have children look at the 4 groups of 3 counters. Show how to count by ones to find the total, 12. Next, demonstrate how skip counting by threes is just a faster way to find the same total, 12.

▶ **Share and Show** • Guided Practice

Exercises 3–5 connect to the learning model.

After children solve each problem, have volunteers share their solutions with the class. Encourage them to defend their solutions. Ask questions such as the following.

• **What does your picture look like?**

• **What skip counting pattern does your picture show?**

Go Deeper 〔MATHEMATICAL PRACTICES〕

Have children each choose one problem on this page and rewrite the problem so that there is a greater number of equal groups. Then have children describe how to solve the problem.

✔ **Quick Check** 〔RtI〕

If	a child misses Exercises 3 and 4

Then	**Differentiate Instruction** with

• RtI Tier 1 Activity, p. 157B
• Reteach 3.10
• Soar to Success Math 60.02

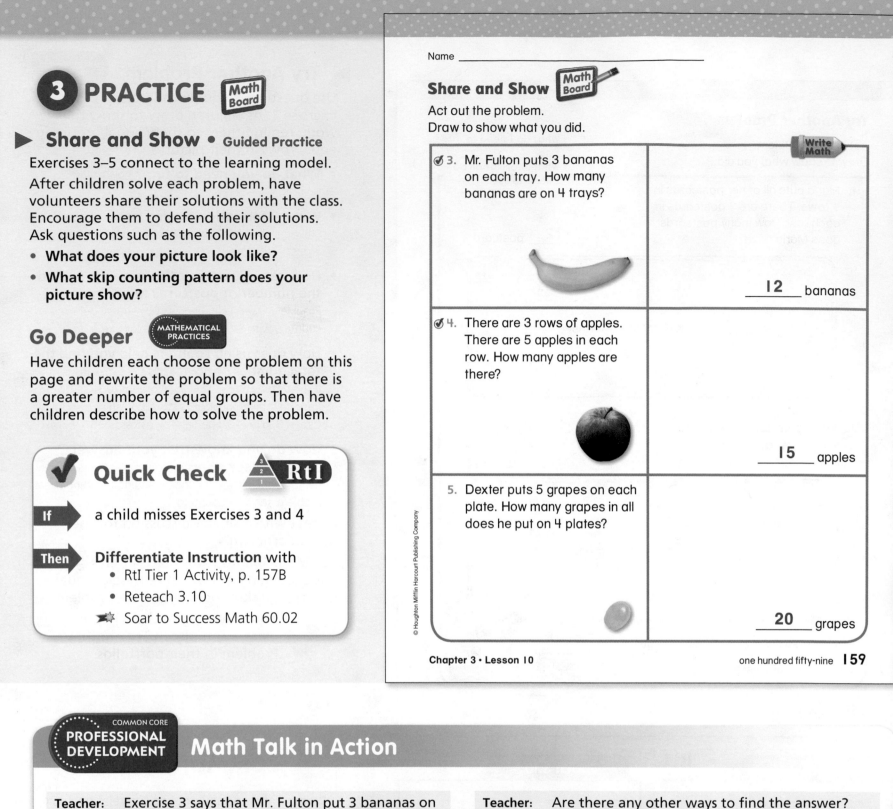

Name _____

Share and Show 〔Math Board〕

Act out the problem.
Draw to show what you did.

☑ 3. Mr. Fulton puts 3 bananas on each tray. How many bananas are on 4 trays?

_____12_____ bananas

☑ 4. There are 3 rows of apples. There are 5 apples in each row. How many apples are there?

_____15_____ apples

5. Dexter puts 5 grapes on each plate. How many grapes in all does he put on 4 plates?

_____20_____ grapes

Chapter 3 • Lesson 10   one hundred fifty-nine **159**

© Houghton Mifflin Harcourt Publishing Company

〔COMMON CORE PROFESSIONAL DEVELOPMENT〕 **Math Talk in Action**

Teacher:	Exercise 3 says that Mr. Fulton put 3 bananas on each of 4 trays. What are some ways we can use to find how many bananas there are?
Matt:	We can draw a diagram. There are 3 bananas on each tray, so there are 3 in each row. There are 4 trays, so there are 4 rows. I would draw a picture like this:

Teacher:	Are there any other ways to find the answer?
Anna:	I would rather use blocks. I would just use a ones block for each banana. I would put 4 rows of 3 ones blocks in each row.
Chad:	I think it would be easier to just write numbers, like this: 3 + 3 + 3 + 3. That is 12.
Kaya:	Or, we could just skip count by threes: 3, 6, 9, 12. There are 12 bananas in all.
Teacher:	You are all correct! There are many different ways to solve a problem.

On Your Own

Choose a way to solve.
Write or draw to explain.

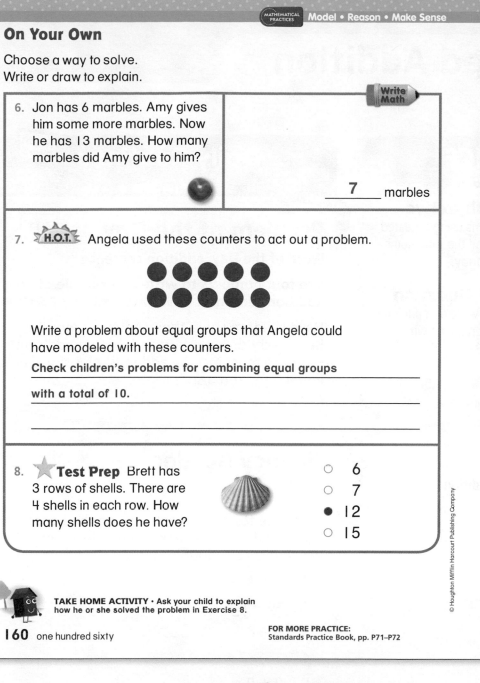

6. Jon has 6 marbles. Amy gives him some more marbles. Now he has 13 marbles. How many marbles did Amy give to him?

_____7_____ marbles

7. **H.O.T.** Angela used these counters to act out a problem.

Write a problem about equal groups that Angela could have modeled with these counters.

Check children's problems for combining equal groups

_____

with a total of 10.

_____

_____

8. ⭐ **Test Prep** Brett has 3 rows of shells. There are 4 shells in each row. How many shells does he have?

- ○ 6
- ○ 7
- ● 12
- ○ 15

TAKE HOME ACTIVITY · Ask your child to explain how he or she solved the problem in Exercise 8.

160 one hundred sixty

FOR MORE PRACTICE:
Standards Practice Book, pp. P71–P72

© Houghton Mifflin Harcourt Publishing Company

▶ **On Your Own** • Independent Practice

Unlock the Problem In Exercise 6, children need to solve for a missing addend.

H.O.T. Problem Exercise 7 requires children to use higher order thinking skills as they write a real-life problem that can be translated to the concrete representation shown with counters.

• **How can you skip count to solve Angela's problem?** Possible answer: 5, 10

⭐ Test Prep Coach

Test Prep Coach helps teachers to identify common errors that children can make.

In Exercise 8, if children selected:

- **6,** they did not understand the problem.
- **7,** they added 3 and 4.
- **15,** they used 5 shells in each row.

4 SUMMARIZE (MATHEMATICAL PRACTICES)

Essential Question

How can acting it out help when solving a problem about equal groups? Possible answer: Acting it out helps me skip count the equal groups to find the total.

Math Journal

Draw 3 rows with 2 counters in each row. Write a word problem that can be acted out using these counters.

Differentiated Instruction · INDEPENDENT ACTIVITIES

Grab-and-Go!™
Differentiated Centers Kit

Activities
Way to Go!

Children complete blue Activity Card 1 by using doubles to add.

Literature
Doubles Fun on the Farm

Children read the book and add equal groups to make doubles.

Digital Path

- ☑ Animated Math Models
- *i*T *i*Tools
- MM HMH Mega Math
- ⭐ Soar to Success Math
- GO eStudent Edition

Algebra • Repeated Addition

LESSON AT A GLANCE

Common Core Standard
Work with equal groups of objects to gain foundations for multiplication.
CC.2.OA.4 Use addition to find the total number of objects arranged in rectangular arrays with up to 5 rows and up to 5 columns; write an equation to express the total as a sum of equal addends.

Lesson Objective
Write equations using repeated addition to find the total number of objects in arrays.

Essential Question
How can you write an addition sentence for problems with equal groups?

Materials
MathBoard, two-color counters

Digital Path

MM HMH Mega Math

GO MATH eStudent Edition

COMMON CORE PROFESSIONAL DEVELOPMENT
About the Math

Teaching for Depth

In this lesson, children write repeated addition sentences about a group of objects arranged in multiple rows of equal numbers of objects.

Guide children to first recognize that the arrangement has the same number of objects in each row. Have them describe what they see in the arrangement. They may find it helpful to count the objects in each row to better understand that it is made up of equal groups. Then have them identify how many rows of equal groups make up the arrangement.

Understanding repeated addition will help children build a foundation for learning multiplication in later grades.

 PODCASTING
Professional Development Video Podcasts

Daily Routines
Common Core

SPIRAL REVIEW

Problem of the Day
eTransparency **3.11**

Word of the Day addition sentence

Use four numbers to write an example of an addition sentence. Possible answer: $3 + 4 + 5 = 12$

Have children share their sentences aloud. Be sure children understand that an addition sentence must include addends, plus signs, an equal sign, and a sum.

Fluency Builder
Basic Facts

Write the following problems on the board. Have children solve. Ask them to identify which facts are doubles facts.

1. $4 + 4 = $ _____8_____
2. $10 - 4 = $ _____6_____
3. $9 + 8 = $ _____17_____
4. $15 - 7 = $ _____8_____
5. $9 + 9 = $ _____18_____
6. $17 - 8 = $ _____9_____
7. $3 + 3 = $ _____6_____

Differentiated Instruction Activities

(ELL) Language Support
Auditory / Visual · Small Group

Strategy: Model Language

- Children can learn correct pronunciation and sentence structure by listening to and repeating words and sentences modeled by the teacher or other native speakers.

- Draw a row of five circles on the board. Tell children that you have drawn five objects in one row. Place your finger below the first circle and move across to the fifth circle. Say the following sentence and have children repeat after you: **This is one row of five objects.**

- Have children draw 2 rows of 4 objects. Then have them describe their drawings in their own words.

See **ELL** Activity Guide for leveled activities.

Enrich
Interpersonal / Visual · Partners

Materials two-color counters

- Write the following riddle on the board.

  I have 10 counters. How many equal rows of counters will show the total number of counters?

- Ask children to use counters to solve the riddle. Encourage them to find two different ways to arrange the counters to match the riddle. Possible answers: 5 rows of 2 counters in each row, or 2 rows of 5 counters in each row.

- Have children repeat the activity with a total of 12 counters.

 **RtI Response to Intervention**

Reteach Tier 1
Kinesthetic / Visual · Whole Class / Small Group

Materials connecting cubes

- Have children make 4 rows of cubes with 3 cubes in each row. Say: **We will write an addition sentence to show how many cubes there are.**

- Have children count the number of cubes in the first row. 3 cubes Write the number on the board. Repeat for the other 3 rows, writing a plus sign between each 3 to show the repeated addition: 3 + 3 + 3 + 3.

- Then have children count the number of rows. Discuss that there are four 3s in the addition sentence on the board because the model has 4 rows of 3 cubes each.

- Guide children to find the sum for the addition sentence. 12 You may wish to have children count the individual cubes to check the answer.

Tier 2
Visual · Small Group

Materials connecting cubes

- Show children 3 rows of cubes with 2 cubes in each row.

- Ask: **How many cubes are in the first row?** 2 cubes **How many cubes are in the second row?** 2 cubes **How many cubes are in the third row?** 2 cubes Record children's answers on the board as repeated addition: 2 + 2 + 2.

- Have children skip count by twos to find the sum. Write = 6 on the board to complete the repeated addition sentence. Have children count the individual cubes to check the answer.

- Discuss with children that there are three 2s in the addition sentence on the board because the model has 3 rows of 2 cubes each. Read the addition sentence aloud and say: **3 rows of 2 cubes each are 6 cubes in all.**

1 ENGAGE

Access Prior Knowledge Draw two rows of four objects.

- **How many objects are in each row?** 4 objects
- **How many rows are there?** 2 rows
- **How many objects are there in all?** 8 objects

2 TEACH and TALK 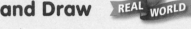 HMH Mega Math

▶ **Listen and Draw** REAL WORLD

Materials two-color counters

Read the following problem.

Clayton has 3 rows of trading cards. There are 5 cards in each row. How many trading cards does Clayton have?

Have children use counters to model the problem.

- **How many rows did you make with the counters?** 3 rows
- **Why did you place 5 counters in each row?** Possible answer: There are 5 trading cards in each row, so I used a counter for each trading card.

Have children draw a picture of their models.

- **Why is it important to draw 5 items in each row?** Possible answer: Clayton has 5 cards in each row. If I do not draw 5 items in each row, I might get the wrong answer.
- **How many trading cards does Clayton have?** 15 trading cards

Use **Math Talk** to focus on children's understanding of how to use models and pictures to find solutions to problems involving repeated addition.

COMMON CORE

CC.2.OA.4 Use addition to find the total number of objects arranged in rectangular arrays with up to 5 rows and up to 5 columns; write an equation to express the total as a sum of equal addends.

Name _____

Algebra • Repeated Addition   Lesson 3.11

Essential Question How can you write an addition sentence for problems with equal groups?

COMMON CORE STANDARD CC.2.OA.4
Work with equal groups of objects to gain foundations for multiplication.

Listen and Draw REAL WORLD

Use counters to model the problem. **Check children's drawings.**
Then draw a picture of your model. **The answer is 15 trading cards.**

Math Talk: Possible answer: I skip counted by 5 three times: 5, 10, 15. So, there are 15 counters in my model.

Math Talk
Describe how you found the number of counters in your model.
MATHEMATICAL PRACTICES

FOR THE TEACHER • Read the following problem and have children first model the problem with counters and then draw a picture of their models. Clayton has 3 rows of trading cards. There are 5 cards in each row. How many trading cards does Clayton have?

© Houghton Mifflin Harcourt Publishing Company

Chapter 3   one hundred sixty-one **161**

Standards Practice 3.11   **Common Core**   SPIRAL REVIEW

Name _____

Algebra • Repeated Addition   Lesson 3.11

COMMON CORE STANDARD CC.2.OA.4
Work with equal groups of objects to gain foundations for multiplication.

Find the number of shapes in each row.
Complete the addition sentence to find the total.

1.
3 rows of _4_
$4 + 4 + 4 = 12$

2.
2 rows of _5_
$5 + 5 = 10$

3.
4 rows of _4_
$4 + 4 + 4 + 4 = 16$

4.
4 rows of _5_
$5 + 5 + 5 + 5 = 20$

PROBLEM SOLVING REAL WORLD

Solve. Write or draw to explain.

5. A classroom has 3 rows of desks. There are 5 desks in each row. How many desks are there altogether?

_15_ desks

Chapter 3   seventy-three P73

Lesson Check (CC.2.OA.4)   TEST PREP

1. A scrapbook has 4 pages. There are 2 stickers on each page. How many stickers are there in all?
   - ○ 4
   - ○ 6
   - ● 8
   - ○ 10

2. Ben makes 5 rows of coins. He puts 3 coins in each row. How many coins are there in all?
   - ○ 9
   - ○ 12
   - ● 15
   - ○ 18

Spiral Review (CC.2.OA.2, CC.2.NBT.2, CC.2.NBT.3)

3. There are 5 apples and 4 oranges. How many pieces of fruit are there? (Lesson 3.1)
   - ○ 10
   - ● 9
   - ○ 8
   - ○ 1

4. Which group of numbers shows counting by tens? (Lesson 1.9)
   - ○ 35, 40, 45, 50, 55
   - ● 40, 50, 60, 70, 80
   - ○ 65, 64, 63, 62, 61
   - ○ 70, 71, 72, 73, 74

5. Which is a way to write the number 260? (Lesson 2.6)
   - ○ twenty-six
   - ○ two hundred six
   - ○ two hundred sixteen
   - ● two hundred sixty

6. Which has the same sum as 7 + 5? (Lesson 3.5)
   - ○ 10 + 4
   - ○ 10 + 3
   - ● 10 + 2
   - ○ 10 + 1

P74 seventy-four

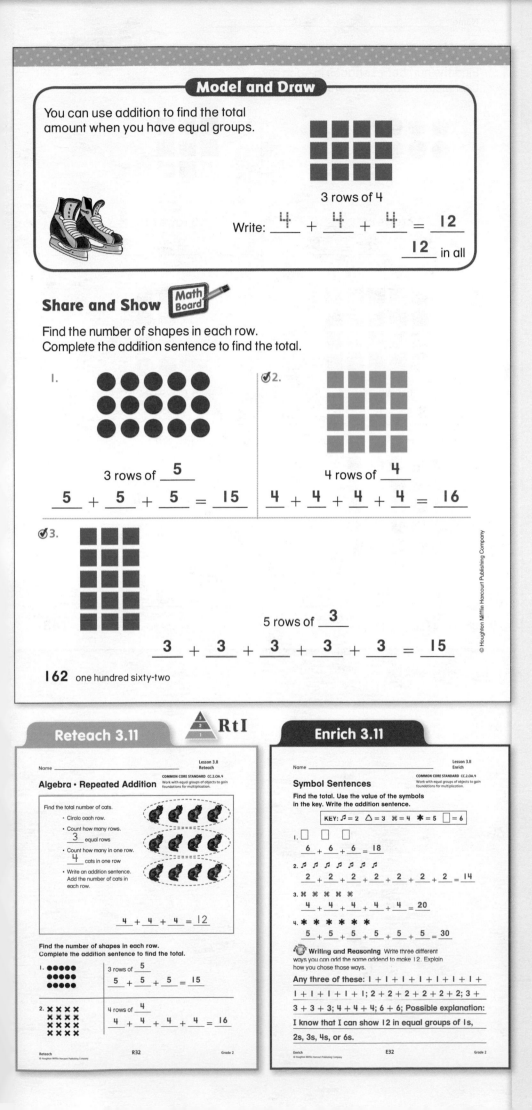

Model and Draw

You can use addition to find the total amount when you have equal groups.

3 rows of 4

Write: $\underline{4} + \underline{4} + \underline{4} = \underline{12}$

$\underline{12}$ in all

Share and Show

Find the number of shapes in each row.
Complete the addition sentence to find the total.

1.

3 rows of $\underline{5}$

$\underline{5} + \underline{5} + \underline{5} = \underline{15}$

2.

4 rows of $\underline{4}$

$\underline{4} + \underline{4} + \underline{4} + \underline{4} = \underline{16}$

3.

5 rows of $\underline{3}$

$\underline{3} + \underline{3} + \underline{3} + \underline{3} + \underline{3} = \underline{15}$

162 one hundred sixty-two

© Houghton Mifflin Harcourt Publishing Company

Reteach 3.11

Name _____
Lesson 3.11 Reteach

Algebra · Repeated Addition
COMMON CORE STANDARD CC.2.OA.4
Work with equal groups of objects to gain foundations for multiplication.

Find the total number of cats.
- Circle each row.
- Count how many rows.
  $\underline{3}$ equal rows.
- Count how many in one row.
  $\underline{4}$ cats in one row.
- Write an addition sentence. Add the number of cats in each row.

$\underline{4} + \underline{4} + \underline{4} = \underline{12}$

Find the number of shapes in each row.
Complete the addition sentence to find the total.

1.
3 rows of $\underline{5}$
$\underline{5} + \underline{5} + \underline{5} = \underline{15}$

2.
4 rows of $\underline{4}$
$\underline{4} + \underline{4} + \underline{4} + \underline{4} = \underline{16}$

Reteach
© Houghton Mifflin Harcourt Publishing Company
R32
Grade 2

Enrich 3.11

Name _____
Lesson 3.11 Enrich

Symbol Sentences
COMMON CORE STANDARD CC.2.OA.4
Work with equal groups of objects to gain foundations for multiplication.

Find the total. Use the value of the symbols in the key. Write the addition sentence.

KEY: ♪ = 2 △ = 3 ⌘ = 4 ✳ = 5 ☐ = 6

1. ☐ ☐ ☐
$\underline{6} + \underline{6} + \underline{6} = \underline{18}$

2. ♪ ♪ ♪ ♪ ♪ ♪ ♪
$\underline{2} + \underline{2} + \underline{2} + \underline{2} + \underline{2} + \underline{2} + \underline{2} = \underline{14}$

3. ⌘ ⌘ ⌘ ⌘ ⌘
$\underline{4} + \underline{4} + \underline{4} + \underline{4} + \underline{4} = \underline{20}$

4. ✳ ✳ ✳ ✳ ✳ ✳
$\underline{5} + \underline{5} + \underline{5} + \underline{5} + \underline{5} + \underline{5} = \underline{30}$

Writing and Reasoning Write three different ways you can add the same addend to make 12. Explain how you chose those ways.

Any three of these: 1 + 1 + 1 + 1 + 1 + 1 + 1 + 1 + 1 + 1 + 1 + 1; 2 + 2 + 2 + 2 + 2 + 2; 3 + 3 + 3 + 3; 4 + 4 + 4; 6 + 6; Possible explanation:
I know that I can show 12 in equal groups of 1s, 2s, 3s, 4s, or 6s.

Enrich
© Houghton Mifflin Harcourt Publishing Company
E32
Grade 2

Model and Draw

MATHEMATICAL PRACTICES

Work through the model with children. Point out that each row has an equal number of tiles.

- **Why are there three 4s written as addends in the number sentence?** Possible answer: Each 4 stands for the four tiles in each of the three rows.

- **Why do you think the number sentence 4 + 4 + 4 = 12 is called repeated addition?** Possible answer: The number of tiles in each row is equal, so the number 4 repeats.

3 PRACTICE

Share and Show • Guided Practice

Exercises 1–3 connect to the learning model.

- **How did you find the total in Exercise 1?** Possible answer: I counted 5 circles in each row. I then added 5 plus 5 plus 5 to get the total of 15.

Use Exercises 2 and 3 for **Quick Check**. Children should use their MathBoards to show their solutions to these exercises.

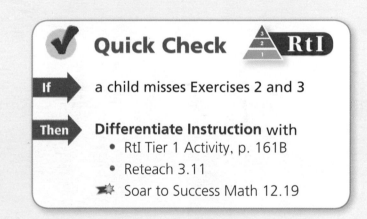

✓ Quick Check

If a child misses Exercises 2 and 3

Then Differentiate Instruction with
- RtI Tier 1 Activity, p. 161B
- Reteach 3.11
- Soar to Success Math 12.19

⚠ COMMON ERRORS

Error Children may forget to add all the numbers repeated in the addition sentence.

Example In Exercise 3, children add 3 + 3 + 3 + 3 + 3 = 12.

Springboard to Learning Have children circle the numbers as they add them and write the sum. For example, they would circle 3 + 3 and write 6. Then they would circle the next 3 and write 9. Have children continue to circle and add until they have added all the addends.

If children answer Exercises 2 and 3 correctly, assign Exercises 4–8.

Go Deeper

To extend their thinking, have children write a story problem involving equal groups. Give children the following repeated addition sentence: 5 + 5 + 5 + 5 = 20. Ask them to write a story problem for the addition sentence and draw rows of equal groups to illustrate it. Have volunteers read their story problems to the class. Repeat the activity for the addition sentence 4 + 4 + 4 + 4 + 4 = 20.

Name _____

On Your Own

Find the number of shapes in each row.
Complete the addition sentence to find the total.

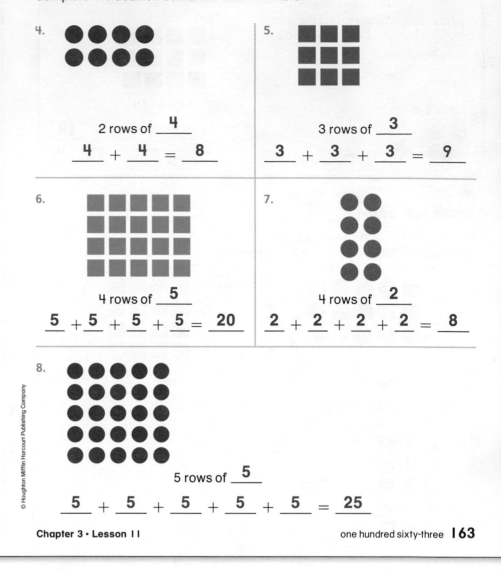

4.

2 rows of ___4___

___4___ + ___4___ = ___8___

5.

3 rows of ___3___

___3___ + ___3___ + ___3___ = ___9___

6.

4 rows of ___5___

___5___ + ___5___ + ___5___ + ___5___ = ___20___

7.

4 rows of ___2___

___2___ + ___2___ + ___2___ + ___2___ = ___8___

8.

5 rows of ___5___

___5___ + ___5___ + ___5___ + ___5___ + ___5___ = ___25___

© Houghton Mifflin Harcourt Publishing Company

Chapter 3 • Lesson 11   one hundred sixty-three **163**

PROBLEM SOLVING REAL WORLD

 Write Math

Solve. Write or draw to explain.

9. Mrs. Chen makes 5 rows of chairs. She puts 2 chairs in each row. How many chairs does Mrs. Chen use?

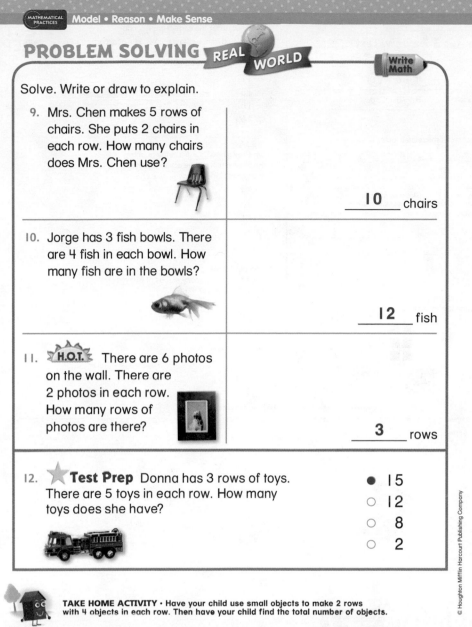

__10__ chairs

10. Jorge has 3 fish bowls. There are 4 fish in each bowl. How many fish are in the bowls?

__12__ fish

11. **H.O.T.** There are 6 photos on the wall. There are 2 photos in each row. How many rows of photos are there?

__3__ rows

12. ⭐ **Test Prep** Donna has 3 rows of toys. There are 5 toys in each row. How many toys does she have?

- ● 15
- ○ 12
- ○ 8
- ○ 2

TAKE HOME ACTIVITY · Have your child use small objects to make 2 rows with 4 objects in each row. Then have your child find the total number of objects.

164 one hundred sixty-four

FOR EXTRA PRACTICE: Standards Practice Book, p. P76

FOR MORE PRACTICE: Standards Practice Book, pp. P73–P74

▶ Problem Solving

Have children read Exercises 9 and 10. Ask children to describe how they will solve each problem.

H.O.T. Problem Exercise 11 requires children to use higher order thinking skills to find the number of rows of equal items, instead of the number of items in all.

⭐ Test Prep Coach

Test Prep Coach helps teachers to identify common errors that children can make.

In Exercise 12, if children selected:

- **12,** they used 3 rows of 4 toys in each row.
- **8,** they added the number of toys in each row to the number of rows.
- **2,** they subtracted the number of rows from the number of toys in each row.

4 SUMMARIZE

Essential Question

How can you write an addition sentence for problems with equal groups? Possible answer: I count the number of items in a row and the number of rows. I write an addition sentence by repeating the number of items in a row the same number of times as there are rows.

Math Journal

Explain how to write an addition sentence for a picture of 4 rows with 3 items in each row.

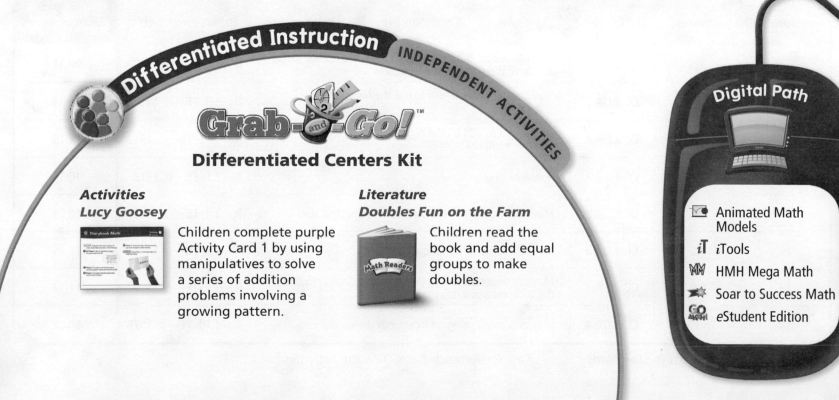

Differentiated Instruction — INDEPENDENT ACTIVITIES

Grab-and-Go!
Differentiated Centers Kit

Activities
Lucy Goosey

Children complete purple Activity Card 1 by using manipulatives to solve a series of addition problems involving a growing pattern.

Literature
Doubles Fun on the Farm

Children read the book and add equal groups to make doubles.

Digital Path

- 📺 Animated Math Models
- *iT* iTools
- 𝓜𝓜 HMH Mega Math
- ⭐ Soar to Success Math
- 🏁 eStudent Edition

Chapter 3
Review/Test

Summative Assessment

Use the **Chapter Review/Test** to assess children's progress in Chapter 3.

You may want to review with children the essential question for the chapter.

Chapter Essential Question

How can you use patterns and strategies to find sums and differences for basic facts?

Ask the following questions to focus children's thinking:

- **What are some strategies for remembering addition and subtraction facts?**
- **How are addition and subtraction related?**

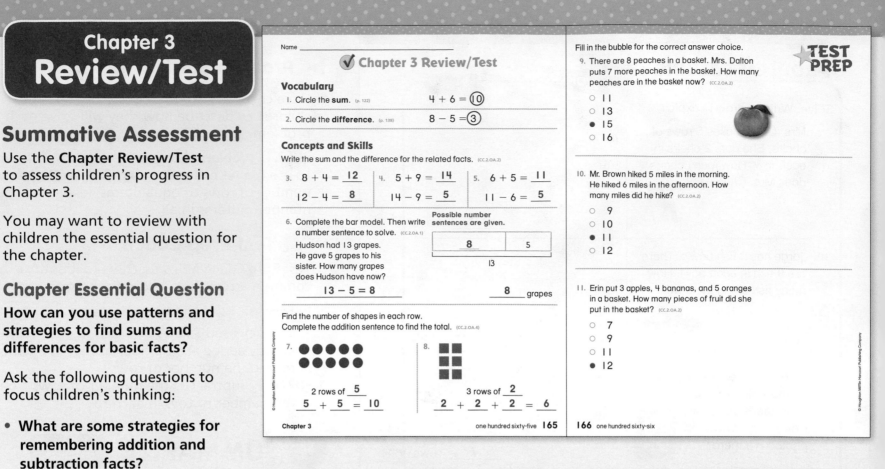

Name _____

✓ Chapter 3 Review/Test

Vocabulary

1. Circle the **sum**. (p. 122) $4 + 6 = \textcircled{10}$

2. Circle the **difference**. (p. 139) $8 - 5 = \textcircled{3}$

Concepts and Skills

Write the sum and the difference for the related facts. (CC.2.OA.2)

3. $8 + 4 = \underline{12}$
   $12 - 4 = \underline{8}$

4. $5 + 9 = \underline{14}$
   $14 - 9 = \underline{5}$

5. $6 + 5 = \underline{11}$
   $11 - 6 = \underline{5}$

6. Complete the bar model. Then write a number sentence to solve. (CC.2.OA.1)

   Hudson had 13 grapes. He gave 5 grapes to his sister. How many grapes does Hudson have now?

   Possible number sentences are given.

8	5
   13

   $\underline{13 - 5 = 8}$ $\underline{8}$ grapes

Find the number of shapes in each row. Complete the addition sentence to find the total. (CC.2.OA.4)

7. ●●●●●
   ●●●●●
   2 rows of $\underline{5}$
   $\underline{5} + \underline{5} = \underline{10}$

8.
   3 rows of $\underline{2}$
   $\underline{2} + \underline{2} + \underline{2} = \underline{6}$

Chapter 3   one hundred sixty-five **165**

Fill in the bubble for the correct answer choice.   ⭐ **TEST PREP**

9. There are 8 peaches in a basket. Mrs. Dalton puts 7 more peaches in the basket. How many peaches are in the basket now? (CC.2.OA.2)
   - ○ 11
   - ○ 13
   - ● 15
   - ○ 16

10. Mr. Brown hiked 5 miles in the morning. He hiked 6 miles in the afternoon. How many miles did he hike? (CC.2.OA.2)
    - ○ 9
    - ○ 10
    - ● 11
    - ○ 12

11. Erin put 3 apples, 4 bananas, and 5 oranges in a basket. How many pieces of fruit did she put in the basket? (CC.2.OA.2)
    - ○ 7
    - ○ 9
    - ○ 11
    - ● 12

166 one hundred sixty-six

✓ Data-Driven Decision Making ▲ RtI

Based on the results of the Chapter Review/Test use the following resources to review skills.

Item	Lesson	*CCSS	Common Error	Intervene With	Soar to Success Math
3–5	3.5	CC.2.OA.2	May not realize that the two problems are related facts and have the same whole and parts	R—3.5; TE—p. 137B	29.31
6	3.8	CC.2.OA.1	May not understand how to use the bar model to help solve	R—3.8; TE—p. 149B	29.33
7, 8	3.11	CC.2.OA.4	May forget to add all the numbers repeated in the addition sentence	R—3.11; TE—p. 161B	12.19
9, 10	3.1	CC.2.OA.2	May add incorrectly	R—3.1; TE—p. 121B	10.19
11	3.4	CC.2.OA.2	May not add the third addend to find the total sum	R—3.4; TE—p. 133B	10.24
12	3.6	CC.2.OA.2	May add rather than subtract	R—3.6; TE—p. 141B	11.15
13	3.9	CC.2.OA.1	May not understand that they need to subtract to find the difference in a comparison problem	R—3.9; TE—p. 153B	11.17
14	3.10	CC.2.OA.4	May skip count using an incorrectly drawn diagram	R—3.10; TE—p. 157B	60.02

*CCSS—Common Core State Standards   **Key: R—Reteach Book; TE—RtI Activities**

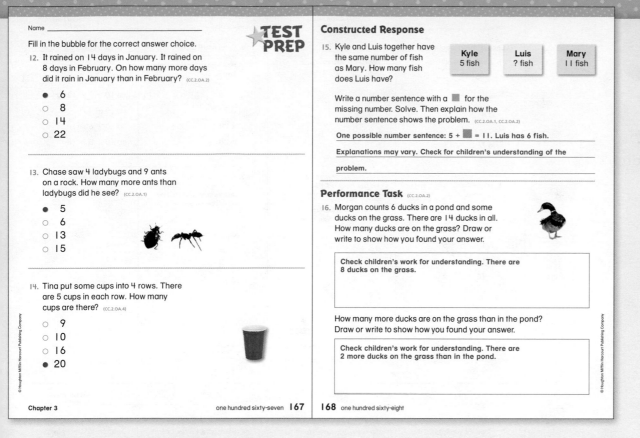

Name _____

Fill in the bubble for the correct answer choice.

TEST PREP

12. It rained on 14 days in January. It rained on 8 days in February. On how many more days did it rain in January than in February? (CC.2.OA.2)
- ● 6
- ○ 8
- ○ 14
- ○ 22

13. Chase saw 4 ladybugs and 9 ants on a rock. How many more ants than ladybugs did he see? (CC.2.OA.1)
- ● 5
- ○ 6
- ○ 13
- ○ 15

14. Tina put some cups into 4 rows. There are 5 cups in each row. How many cups are there? (CC.2.OA.4)
- ○ 9
- ○ 10
- ○ 16
- ● 20

Constructed Response

15. Kyle and Luis together have the same number of fish as Mary. How many fish does Luis have?

Kyle	Luis	Mary
5 fish	? fish	11 fish

Write a number sentence with a ■ for the missing number. Solve. Then explain how the number sentence shows the problem. (CC.2.OA.1, CC.2.OA.2)

One possible number sentence: 5 + ■ = 11. Luis has 6 fish.

Explanations may vary. Check for children's understanding of the problem.

Performance Task (CC.2.OA.2)

16. Morgan counts 6 ducks in a pond and some ducks on the grass. There are 14 ducks in all. How many ducks are on the grass? Draw or write to show how you found your answer.

> Check children's work for understanding. There are 8 ducks on the grass.

How many more ducks are on the grass than in the pond? Draw or write to show how you found your answer.

> Check children's work for understanding. There are 2 more ducks on the grass than in the pond.

Constructed Response

Score children's responses with a 2-1-0 rubric (see *Assessment Guide*). A level 2 response would include children's answers showing an accurate number sentence with a box for the missing addend and an explanation that shows children's understanding of the problem.

Performance Task

Use performance indicators, scoring rubric, and DOK level to evaluate conceptual understanding.

Performance Indicators

A child with a Level 2 paper:

____ recognizes that the whole, 14 ducks in all, and one part, 6 ducks in a pond, are given and that the other part, the number of ducks on the grass, must be found.

____ correctly solves for the missing part: 8 ducks on the grass.

____ recognizes the second question as a comparison problem in which both the larger quantity, 8 ducks on the grass, and the smaller quantity, 6 ducks in a pond, are given, and the difference must be found.

____ correctly solves the comparison problem: there are 2 more ducks on the grass than in the pond.

Performance Assessment — **Depth of Knowledge**

Performance Task	DOK Level
	2

Performance Task Scoring Rubric

2	**Generally accurate, complete, and clear:** All of the parts of the task are successfully completed. There is evidence of clear understanding of the key concepts and procedures. Child's work shows that all answers are correct or reasonable.
1	**Partially accurate:** Some of the parts of the task are successfully completed; other parts are attempted and their intent addressed, but they are not completed.
0	**Not accurate, complete, and clear:** No part of the task is completed with any success. There is little, if any, evidence that the child understands key concepts and procedures.

Performance Assessment
Chapters 3–6

See *Assessment Guide* for Performance Tasks to be completed at the end of each critical area.

 Performance Task may be used for portfolios.

Summative Assessment

Use the **Chapter Test** to assess children's progress in Chapter 3.

Chapter Tests are provided in multiple-choice and mixed-response format in the *Assessment Guide*.

 Chapter 3 Test is available online.

Name _____ Chapter 3 Test Page 1

Choose the correct answer.

1. What is the sum?

$$5 + 2$$

○ 4
○ 5
○ 6
● 7

2. What is the difference?

$$13 - 9$$

● 4
○ 5
○ 6
○ 7

3. Which shows a way to find the difference?

$$15 - 7 = \_\_\_$$

● 10 − 2 = 8
○ 10 − 5 = 5
○ 10 − 7 = 3
○ 10 − 8 = 2

4. Jan has 7 stickers. Her brother gives her 6 more stickers.

Which doubles fact can you use to find how many stickers Jan has now?

○ 5 + 5 = 10
● 7 + 7 = 14
○ 8 + 8 = 16
○ 9 + 9 = 18

Assessment Guide
© Houghton Mifflin Harcourt Publishing Company
AG65
Form A • Multiple Choice

Name _____ Chapter 3 Test Page 2

5. Owen puts 4 apples in each basket. There are 6 baskets. How many apples are there in all?

○ 16
○ 20
● 24
○ 28

6. Which shows a way to find the sum?

$$4 + 8 = \_\_\_$$

● 10 + 2 = 12
○ 10 + 4 = 14
○ 10 + 6 = 16
○ 10 + 8 = 18

7. Ava grows 3 red flowers, 4 yellow flowers, and 4 purple flowers in her garden. How many flowers does Ava grow in all?

○ 7
○ 8
○ 10
● 11

8. What is the sum?

$$4 + 5 + 7 = \_\_\_$$

○ 9
○ 11
● 16
○ 17

Assessment Guide
© Houghton Mifflin Harcourt Publishing Company
AG66
Form A • Multiple Choice

Name _____ Chapter 3 Test Page 3

9. There were 8 ants on a rock. Some more ants joined them. Then there were 13 ants on the rock. How many ants joined them?

○ 4
● 5
○ 13
○ 21

10. What is the missing number in the related subtraction fact?

$$9 + 3 = 12$$
$$12 - 9 = \square$$

○ 9
○ 6
○ 4
● 3

11. Eli has 13 marbles. Amber has 6 marbles. How many more marbles does Eli have than Amber?

● 7
○ 8
○ 10
○ 19

12. Look at the picture. What is the total number of shapes?

○ 9
● 12
○ 14
○ 16

Assessment Guide
© Houghton Mifflin Harcourt Publishing Company
AG67
Form A • Multiple Choice

Name _____ Chapter 3 Test Page 4

13. David has 7 pencils in his pencil case. He has 1 pencil in his desk. How many pencils does David have?

○ 6
○ 7
● 8
○ 9

14. Bob has 15 markers and 7 crayons. How many more markers than crayons does Bob have?

○ 7
● 8
○ 12
○ 15

15. There are 11 books on a shelf. Then Reba takes some books off the shelf. Now there are 4 books on the shelf. How many books did Reba take off the shelf?

○ 15
○ 10
○ 8
● 7

16. Peter sees 8 dogs. Beth sees 1 more dog than Peter. How many dogs do they see in all?

○ 18
● 17
○ 16
○ 14

Assessment Guide
© Houghton Mifflin Harcourt Publishing Company
AG68
Form A • Multiple Choice

✔ Data-Driven Decision Making ▲ RtI

Item	Lesson	*CCSS	Common Error	Intervene With	Soar to Success Math
1, 13	3.2	CC.2.OA.2	May not count on to add	R—3.2; TE—p. 125B	10.19, 10.23
2, 14	3.6	CC.2.OA.2	May subtract incorrectly	R—3.6; TE—p. 141B	11.15
3, 15	3.7	CC.2.OA.2	May not understand how to use tens facts to subtract	R—3.7; TE—p. 145B	
4, 16	3.1	CC.2.OA.2	May not understand how to use doubles facts to add	R—3.1; TE—p. 121B	10.19

*CCSS—Common Core State Standards   **Key: R**—Reteach Book; **TE**—RtI Activities

Name _____

17. Mia puts 5 crackers on each plate. How many crackers does she put on 3 plates?

○ 10
● 15
○ 20
○ 25

18. There are 9 ducks in a pond. Then 5 more ducks go in the pond. How many ducks are in the pond altogether?

○ 11
○ 12
○ 13
● 14

19. What is the sum?

$$\begin{array}{r} 4 \\ 3 \\ + 6 \\ \hline \end{array}$$

● 13
○ 10
○ 9
○ 7

20. Mark picks 11 apples. Anna picks 5 apples. Which number sentence shows how many fewer apples Anna picked than Mark?

○ $16 - 11 = 5$
● $11 - 5 = 6$
○ $11 + 5 = 16$
○ $11 + 6 = 17$

GO ON ▶

Name _____

21. Which shows a related addition fact?

$$13 - 6 = 7$$

● $6 + 7 = 13$
○ $7 + 13 = 20$
○ $7 - 6 = 1$
○ $13 + 6 = 19$

22. Julian had 14 grapes. He gave 5 grapes to Lindsay. How many grapes does Julian have now?

○ 19
○ 11
○ 10
● 9

23. Leah has 8 green apples and 4 red apples. How many apples does Leah have?

○ 4
○ 8
● 12
○ 14

24. Mae has 2 rows of stickers. There are 4 stickers in each row. How many stickers does Mae have?

○ 2
○ 4
○ 6
● 8

STOP

Portfolio Suggestions The portfolio represents the growth, talents, achievements, and reflections of the mathematics learner. Children might spend a short time selecting work samples for their portfolios and completing A Guide to My Math Portfolio from the *Assessment Guide*.

You may want to have children respond to the following questions:

- How do you think you did on this test?
- What do you understand about the chapter that you did not understand before the chapter?
- What would you like to learn more about?

For information about how to organize, share, and evaluate portfolios, see the *Assessment Guide*.

✓ Data-Driven Decision Making ▲ RtI

Item	Lesson	*CCSS	Common Error	Intervene With	Soar to Success Math
5, 17	3.10	CC.2.OA.4	May not know how to solve problems involving equal groups	R—3.10; TE—p. 157B	60.02
6, 18	3.3	CC.2.OA.2	May not understand how to make a ten	R—3.3; TE—p. 129B	10.20
7, 8, 19	3.4	CC.2.OA.2	May not add three addends correctly	R—3.4; TE—p. 133B	10.24
9	3.9	CC.2.OA.1	May not use the correct operation to solve	R—3.9; TE—p. 153B	11.17
10, 21	3.5	CC.2.OA.2	May not understand the term *related fact*	R—3.5; TE—p. 137B	29.31
11, 22, 23	3.8	CC.2.OA.1	May not understand the problem situation	R—3.8; TE—p. 149B	29.33
12, 24	3.11	CC.2.OA.4	May not know how to solve problems involving equal groups	R—3.11; TE—p. 161B	12.19
20	3.9	CC.2.OA.1	May use an incorrect number sentence to solve	R—3.9; TE—p. 153B	11.17

*CCSS—Common Core State Standards   **Key: R**—Reteach Book; **TE**—RtI Activities